'One night with [...] time playboys?'

Rachel continued wryly, 'It had to be a disaster.'

Riccardo drew in a little breath as if she had punched him unexpectedly.

'I see your point,' he admitted levelly. 'What I don't see is why.'

He put a hand on her waist. It felt hot, burning. Suddenly Rachel was having trouble getting her thoughts together.

'Why?' she echoed.

'Why it had to be just one night,' he explained.

Rachel stared at him. Desperately she reminded herself that, however practised he was, she had the measure of him. She might be shaking but she had built some defences in the last nine years. Now she activated them. She pushed at him, head down, outraged.

'Get out of my house.'

He gave ground, but he did not look defeated.

'There's unfinished business between you and me, Rachel. You know it and so do I. Nothing either of us can say will change that.'

Born in London, **Sophie Weston** is a traveller by nature who started writing when she was five. She wrote her first romance when recovering from illness, thinking her travelling was over. She was wrong, but she enjoyed it so much that she has carried on. These days she lives in the heart of the city with two demanding cats and a cherry tree—and travels the world, looking for settings for her stories.

Recent titles by the same author:

AVOIDING MR RIGHT

THE INNOCENT AND THE PLAYBOY

BY
SOPHIE WESTON

MILLS & BOON®

All the characters in this book have no existence outside the imagination of the author, and have no relation whatsoever to anyone bearing the same name or names. They are not even distantly inspired by any individual known or unknown to the author, and all the incidents are pure invention.

*First published in Great Britain 1997
Harlequin Mills & Boon Limited,
Eton House, 18-24 Paradise Road, Richmond, Surrey TW9 1SR*

© Sophie Weston 1997

ISBN 0 263 80153 5

*Set in Times Roman 10 on 10¼ pt.
02-9706-60480 C1*

*Printed and bound in Great Britain
by Mackays of Chatham PLC, Chatham*

CHAPTER ONE

'I WON'T,' yelled Alexandra from the staircase.

Rachel cast a harried look at the kitchen clock. The taxi was due any minute and she had not even checked her briefcase. At the table her stepson, Hugh, was munching his way through an enormous plate of toast and blackcurrant jam, ignoring his sister. No help there, then. Rachel sighed and went out into the hall. She looked up the stairs at her grim-faced stepdaughter.

'Look, I've said no and...'

Alexandra's expression darkened even further. 'You've got no right to say no. You're not even my mother.'

This was a complaint that was appearing in their arguments more and more. Rachel would have found it easier to deal with, she was sure, if she had not had a stepmother herself. As it was, half of her sympathised totally with Alexandra. The other, responsible half knew that an adventurous fifteen-year-old needed rules of conduct more than she needed sympathy. As a result their arguments tended to be protracted.

Heaven help me, today of all days, thought Rachel. She resisted the temptation to look at her watch but it was tough.

'I know I'm not your mother, Alexandra. It makes no difference. Any adult would tell you the same.'

'Theo's an adult and he thinks I should go.'

'Any responsible female adult,' Rachel corrected herself grimly. She hesitated, then, choosing her words with care, said, 'Of course Theo wants you to go. You're a very pretty girl.'

She did not add, as she might well have done, And you're going to inherit half your father's business in less than three years. She did not need to. It was there be-

5

tween them already. Her stepdaughter had not forgotten a word of the disastrous altercation after her last evening out with Theo Judd. Rachel could see it in Alexandra's hot eyes.

Her next words confirmed it. 'You think Theo's after my money.'

Rachel pushed her hair back wearily. It was too long. It needed cutting. She had kept it short for nine years but during these last hectic weeks she had not had time to get it cut.

'I don't know what he's after, Alexandra, and that's the truth.'

'He's too old for me. Go on, say it.'

'Do I have to?'

Alexandra almost stamped her foot. 'You just don't know what it's like.'

And that was a problem too. Rachel knew exactly what it was like to be in love when you were too young and the man you loved was too worldly and sophisticated to recognise how vulnerable you were. In fact, she had worked hard at forgetting for nine years. What was more, she would have said she had succeeded, until Alexandra had decided to make a present of her generous heart to a twenty-four-year-old bartender with a line in flash cars and flashier repartee. Trying to induce a little wariness in her stepdaughter had brought back some memories which could still make Rachel wince.

Sidestepping Alexandra's comment, she said, 'I do know that I would not be much of a guardian if I let you stay out till all hours, God knows where, with a man who is nine years older than you are.'

Alexandra could sidestep difficult issues too.

'Dad was twenty years older than you,' she snarled.

It was true. In spite of her anger and worry, just for a moment Rachel was startled into amusement. 'You've got me there,' she admitted. She leaned her arm on the carved wooden banisters and looked up at her step-daughter straightly. 'Look, Lexy, I know you won't be-lieve me now, but that really was different. Your father and I had both been around a bit. Fifteen and twenty-four is another kettle of fish entirely.'

'You mean I'm a child.'

'No, maybe not a child exactly. But there is a whole world of experiences you have not had yet.'

'And Theo has?'

By the truck-load, if Rachel was any judge. Wisely she did not say that either.

Instead she said, 'Well, he must be well aware of the difference between you and girlfriends of his own age. Even if you aren't.'

Alexandra tossed her head. 'Theo thinks I'm very mature.'

Hell, thought Rachel.

There was a swish of tyres on the wet gravel outside the house. Her taxi had arrived.

Knowing that she was giving in and she should not do it, she said, 'Look, we'll talk about it this evening...'

'Because you've got to rush off to work, right?'

'Because I'm *late* for work,' Rachel said between her teeth. 'Because I'm making a strategy presentation. Because the full board will be there and some of the shareholders aren't happy. Because I have other responsibilities as well as you.'

'You're not responsible for me,' flashed Alexandra. 'I can make my own decisions.'

Rachel sighed. 'Not legally. Look, I've got to go.'

'If my father were alive you wouldn't treat me like this.'

Rachel winced. Even though these were exactly the circumstances which Brian had envisaged when he'd first begged her to marry him, and they'd both thought she had prepared for them, Rachel had been missing him badly in recent days.

The taxi hooted. Rachel stopped glaring at Alexandra and shot into the kitchen. Late as she was, she still checked the briefcase methodically. It was something her own father had taught her to do and she sometimes thought ruefully that she could do it in her sleep. Everything was there.

She pinned up her hair on top of her head without looking in the mirror. Then she stuffed her handbag under her arm and prepared to go.

Hugh looked up from his breakfast. The pile of toast had diminished noticeably, as it always did. So why did he always look as if he were starving? Rachel thought. He saw her worried look and grinned.

'Sock it to them, Super Shark.'

Rachel knew this was meant to be both encouraging and complimentary. She responded accordingly.

'Thank you very much for your support. Hugh...'

He jerked his head at the door. 'Don't worry about her. She'll sort herself out sooner or later.'

'Just as long as it isn't too late,' muttered Rachel, not much comforted.

'Don't worry about it. Lexy can look after herself,' said her sympathetic brother.

'I hope you're right.'

The taxi hooted again, longer.

'Damn. I must go. I'm sorry. I'll see you both to-night,' said Rachel, running.

Too fast, of course. It was blowing a gale outside. The leaves flew up, making her blink against the flying dust. The wind caught at her hastily arranged hair and whipped great hanks of red-gold fronding out of its confining hairpins. She cursed but she did not go back to repair the damage. She had told the children she was late for a board meeting. What she had not told them was that it could just turn out to be the most important meeting of her life.

Now, racing into the waiting taxi, she slipped and fell to one knee on the gravel. She felt the run in her tights at once. But it was too late to go back and change. The unfamiliar taxi driver was already impatient and Rachel was hardly less so. She got into the back seat and slammed the door.

'Bentley's Investment Bank,' she said. 'Old Ship Street.'

All the way to the huge new office block, she could feel the run snaking down her leg. On the sheer dark tights she favoured, it was going to be horribly conspicuous. She would have to keep her legs out of sight under the board table until she could dash out and get another pair. Maybe just before lunch, thought Rachel, running over the timetable in her mind. Then, jumping out of the taxi, she did not duck low enough. Rachel felt her already descending *coiffure* lurch sideways at the impact. It was the final straw.

As the taxi drove off, she swore before turning to steam in through the silent automatic doors.

'Morning, Mrs Gray,' said the security officer, from behind his smart, brass-trimmed desk. He had seen her mishap and could not suppress his grin. 'Bit windy out there.'

Rachel hefted her briefcase under her arm and thrust her free hand distractedly through her hair. Several pins fell out.

'Morning, Geoff. Are they here yet?'

The security guards had the best information network in the bank. Geoff did not pretend to misunderstand.

'The party from the States arrived about ten minutes ago.'

'Oh, hell.'

'Mr Jensen is giving them the tour.'

Rachel stopped fluffing up her hair and scattering pins. 'You mean he knew I hadn't got here?'

Geoff looked wise. 'He was looking for you earlier. Mandy told him you were on your way.'

Mandy was her secretary. Philip Jensen was Rachel's boss—at least on the organisation chart—and he was a panicker.

Rachel sighed. She should have been here an hour ago at least. She had intended to be when she'd put her papers for the meeting into her briefcase last night. But with Alexandra's bombshell at the breakfast table she had temporarily lost sight of her timetable. The fact that it was her own fault did not help. If anything it made it slightly worse.

'*Hell,*' said Rachel again with feeling.

Geoff grinned and opened the small door at the side of the security guards' cubby-hole. They had their own lift to all floors which no one else was supposed to use. The theory was that it should be available at all times in case of a security alert. As a result, it was known to be the fastest route between floors. In addition, it had the advantage that she was unlikely to meet the board and their honoured guests in the unadorned steel box which served the security force. It was against bank policy but, on today of all days, the offer was irresistible.

'Thank you,' said Rachel with real gratitude, and dived into the prohibited lift.

She made it into her secretary's office without encountering anyone else. Mandy looked up and took in her situation in a glance. She swung round on her rotating chair and extracted a new packet of tights from the pile in the stationery cupboard behind her.

'Traffic?' she said.

Rachel dropped the briefcase thankfully. 'Only domestic.'

Mandy pushed the tights across the desk and surveyed her thoughtfully. 'You've got mud on your jacket.'

Rachel looked down. It was true. There was a great splash of it like a wizard's hand across the front.

'I didn't realise. It must have happened when I tripped. Damn.'

Mandy held out a hand. 'Give it to me. I'll have a go with the clothes-brush. You deal with the extremities.'

Rachel shrugged herself out of the jacket. 'My one designer suit,' she said gloomily. 'Only just back from the cleaners.'

Mandy was surveying the dried mud. 'The check jacket is in your office. If all else fails you could wear that.'

The check jacket was an old friend. So old that its black velvet collar showed its age. They both knew it. Rachel sighed again.

'Philip will be furious.'

'Philip is too terrified to be furious,' Mandy said frankly. 'He'll be so relieved to see you, he won't care if you turn up in dungarees. Go on.'

Rachel went swiftly into the ladies' cloakroom, pulling the remaining pins out of her hair as she went. Mandy soon joined her, bearing the check jacket apologetically.

'Designer clothes need designer cleaning. I brushed the mud off but you could still see the shadow.'

Rachel lobbed the ruined tights into the waste-paper basket and smoothed her skirt.

'Thank you for trying.' She straightened up to face her image in the big mirror behind the hand basins and grimaced. 'It's not going to make much difference anyway. My hair needs surgery. I've lost too many pins to put it up properly.'

'Then leave it loose.'

Rachel fluffed out the red-gold fronds doubtfully. 'Not very professional.'

'Better than everyone in the meeting sitting there wondering when it's going to fall down,' Mandy said, ever practical.

Rachel laughed suddenly. 'You're probably right. I don't want to distract them from my beautiful corporate plan.'

She brushed her hair rapidly. Mandy gathered up the scatter of hairpins and silently laid out Rachel's under-used cosmetics. Most of the time Rachel wore no make-up at all unless she was going to some big business reception.

It was Mandy's private opinion that this was a horrible waste. However, Rachel, although in general as friendly and informal a boss as you could wish for, did not encourage this sort of comment. Mandy could never quite work out whether this was because Rachel genu-inely did not know how spectacular she could look when she tried. It seemed unlikely. Sometimes Mandy even suspected that Rachel knew quite well and was, for some obscure reason of her own, terrified by it.

Now Rachel made a face in the mirror, reaching out for the little make-up case. 'Why is painting your face supposed to improve your confidence?'

Mandy perched on the edge of the vanity counter. 'Because it makes you look more like a performer?'

'You mean like a clown?'

'Like a star,' Mandy said reprovingly.

Rachel snorted and wrinkled her nose at her reflection. 'Some hopes.'

So maybe her unawareness of her looks was real. But she had to know how high her professional reputation stood. So why did she not have more self-confidence? Someone somewhere must have done a real number on Rachel, Mandy thought.

She was too tactful to say so, however. Instead, she said, 'Your confidence doesn't need any boosting. Everyone in the bank knows how good you are at your job.'

Rachel laughed. 'That isn't the point. I'm the one who has to believe I'm good. That's what confidence means. And after this morning—' She broke off.

'What went wrong this morning? Homework?'

Rachel ran a small make-up sponge under the tap before replying. A faint frown appeared as she brushed the sponge across the compressed block of pale tan colour.

'No.' She hesitated, then started to sponge on the light make-up with quick, angry strokes. 'It's Alexandra.'

Mandy nodded, unsurprised. She had worked with Rachel all through the last three traumatic years and she did not have to have the family tensions explained to her.

'Being difficult, is she?'

Rachel put the sponge down. 'She thinks she'd like to live with her mother,' she said neutrally. 'Her real mother, that is.'

Mandy was shocked. 'And can she?'

'I don't know. Not unless her mother wants her, that's for sure.'

'She doesn't?'

Rachel picked up a palette of eye-shadows and a small brush. She surveyed herself, hesitating.

'Not up to now. That's why Brian—' She broke off abruptly and leant forward to paint discreet colour onto her eyelids. Mandy bit her lip. When Rachel mentioned her late husband it was usually a sign that she was deeply disturbed.

'How old is Alexandra now?' she asked, tactfully changing the subject.

Rachel gave her a pale grin in the mirror. 'Fifteen going on forty. To judge by this morning's performance, anyway.'

Mandy was surprised. 'How quickly they grow up. I hadn't realised.'

'Nor, according to Alexandra, had I,' Rachel said drily.

'Ah,' said Mandy, enlightened. She had younger sisters. 'She wants to go to a rock concert and you won't let her.'

Rachel's face tightened. 'Something like that.'

'They all do,' Mandy said comfortingly. 'It's just a phase. I had some terrible fights with my father. You grow out of it.'

Rachel flicked the little brush over her other eyelid. 'Do you? I never had any fights like that. Too much of a goody-goody. Never did anything my father wouldn't like,' she confessed.

Except once, said a small voice inside her. Except that last, fatal time when you brought the whole world down on everyone, just because you were determined to show Riccardo di Stefano and his kind that they could not hurt people with impunity.

It was a voice that had been whispering away for three or four days now. It reminded her that even the best-conducted adolescents could make some horrible mistakes. It was a voice she had silenced for nine years and it was disconcerting to find it coming out of the ether now. Especially as it had a disturbing tendency to take her difficult stepdaughter's side in the present argument.

Mandy said comfortably, 'I bet you did. You've just forgotten.' She relieved Rachel of the eye-shadow and handed her a lipstick and lip-brush. 'Alexandra just needs a good fight with authority at the moment. You happen to be the only major authority figure around. Hard on you, but it's not the end of the world. What she needs is a man in her life.'

Rachel shuddered. 'Don't say that. She's jolly nearly got one.'

Mandy was unperturbed. 'We all had boyfriends.'

Rachel paused, the lip-brush arrested halfway to her mouth. Not me, she thought involuntarily. Is that why I'm so bad at dealing with Alexandra? Is it because I never went through the normal stages? Was I just too busy being a good little girl, working hard and winning prizes? Until... The voice again! Why on earth should it start up *now* when she needed all the confidence she could summon up?

She suppressed the voice, applied the lipstick, stepped back and looked at herself critically.

'Well, that will have to do.'

Mandy nodded approval. In spite of the fact that Rachel paid very little attention to her appearance, when you had shining, naturally auburn hair and wide brown eyes, it did not make too much difference, Mandy thought without jealousy. A dash of modest eye-shadow and Rachel's eyes turned the colour of Madeira wine.

'You look gorgeous.'

Rachel sent her a harassed look. 'I wish I looked tidy.' She flicked irritatedly at the loose hair about her shoulders. 'Tidy is efficient. Untidy—well...'

'Philip knows you're efficient,' Mandy soothed.

'It isn't Philip I have to convince.' She looked at her watch. 'Being half an hour late isn't going to help either.'

Mandy laughed and uncurled herself from her perch.

'Don't worry about it. The new boss man has changed all the meetings round, so no one knows who is due to speak when or on what. With a bit of luck no one except Philip will even know.'

Rachel was looking in the mirror, giving a last downward brush to her neat skirt, but this made her look round. 'New boss man?'

'Genghis Khan in person,' Mandy said cheerfully.

Rachel was aware of a quick lurch in her stomach, as if she were still in Geoff's lift and it had hurtled down to the lowest level of the underground car park. You're paranoid, she told herself. And obsessed. This is ancient history. You'd never have remembered it at all if it weren't for the fight with Alexandra.

She took a firm grip on herself and said casually, 'Which Genghis Khan is that?'

'The main man. Leader of the barbarians in person.'

Her stomach sank below car-park level to somewhere around the seabed.

'You don't mean di Stefano?'

Please tell me you don't mean Riccardo Enrico di Stefano, heir to one fortune and personal creator of another five times the size, patron of the arts, darling of the gossip columns and the man who took confidence into a whole new dimension.

But Mandy was grinning. 'Himself.'

Rachel's stomach penetrated the earth's crust without difficulty and began to swirl around in the molten core. She could feel the heat in her face. She even put up a hand. Her cheekbone was warm under the make-up.

She swallowed. 'What—?' Her voice squeaked. Mandy was looking at her curiously. She swallowed and got a grip on her vocal cords. 'What is Riccardo di Stefano doing here? The bank is only a minority investment from his point of view.'

Mandy chuckled. 'Well, from what I saw when I helped Angela with the photocopying, that's all going to change. I'd say he's going to buy us.'

Rachel stared at her, appalled. Mandy misinterpreted the horror.

'Don't worry about it. He'll probably buy your corporate plan as well. More likely to than the old board, if you ask me.'

This could not be happening. Something inside her was turning over like a hibernating beast roused out of ice. Old, deep ice. Rachel could feel the faint internal tremors starting again. They were not exactly unfamiliar, but she had not been aware of them for years. Meanwhile, Mandy, unaware, was giving her an encouraging smile.

'You could be right,' Rachel said faintly.

Mandy patted her on the shoulder. 'Of course I'm right. Now go and broke the agreement.'

There was nothing to be done. If he was here already, all her escape routes were blocked.

'Yes,' said Rachel automatically.

She shrugged herself into the check jacket like a sleepwalker and went to the door. She looked as if someone had hit her with a sandbag, Mandy thought. More encouragement was clearly called for.

'Cheer up, Rachel. Your tights are whole and your jacket is clean. From here on in, today can only get better.'

Rachel stared at her. For an odd moment it seemed as if she were looking over the precipice of a particularly cold and deadly mountain. Then she gave a harsh laugh. 'I wouldn't put money on it.'

It was bitter. It even startled Mandy out of her cheerfulness. Then she said bracingly, 'You'll do fine. Bigwigs have never worried you. The bigger the wig, the cooler you get.'

But Rachel was still looking sick. Mandy had never seen her look like that before. She began to be alarmed.

'You can handle yourself,' Mandy reminded her urgently, putting a hand on her arm. 'You know you can.'

Rachel gave a little jump as if she had been brought back to the present by main force. 'I hope,' she muttered.

The sick look went out of her face. But although she was regaining command of herself there was still that shaken look at the back of her eyes. It was almost as if she had received a bad shock, Mandy thought. Which, of course, was ridiculous. It took more than a visiting troupe of American money-men to shock Rachel. Or, at least, it ought to.

Rachel was thinking the same thing. She pulled her jacket straight and squared her shoulders in the mirror.

'Boardroom?'

Mandy said, 'Well, Mr Jensen said he'd like to see you in his office first.'

I'll just bet he did, thought Rachel. If the biggest shark of them all has turned up in person, Philip will be turning to jelly.

'But they arrived and he went straight to the boardroom. Would you join him—er—soonest?'

Panic stations, interpreted Rachel. She did not say so. She was too close to panic herself.

'Right,' she said.

She went, buried in thought. Confidence, she said to herself. That's the thing to remember. You're good at your job. You know that. Everyone else does. Believe it, why can't you? Play to your strengths.

He must never know you even remember. Almost certainly he won't. It is nine years ago. He must have had dozens of girls before and since. It's ten to one that he forgot the whole thing in days.

She almost convinced herself.

She was still frowning in preoccupation as she went along the executive corridor. It was ankle-deep in an expensive carpet and hung with valuable seascapes. Usually Philip's idea of executive interior decoration made Rachel laugh. Today, however, she barely noticed it.

In fact she was so deep in thought that she did not notice the man coming towards her. That was hardly her fault. Although he was tall and loose-limbed, he moved like a cat. On the sumptuous carpeting his tread was noiseless.

So when a voice said, 'Hi there,' she jumped about a foot in the air and came down with her head spinning.

It was the voice from her very worst dreams. Rachel felt as if someone had thrown ice-water over her. She found herself staring straight into those laughing, green-flecked eyes for the first time in nine years. It felt like yesterday. She stared at him, transfixed.

The man looked amused. 'Rick di Stefano.'

There was not the slightest hint in his voice that he knew they had met before. Rachel registered his open smile: not a glimmer of recognition there. She moistened suddenly dry lips and tried to believe it.

In all those worst dreams of hers Riccardo di Stefano knew her at once. What he did about it varied with the awfulness of the dream but he had never looked at her with the smile of a pleasant stranger.

Rachel gulped. For the first time in years she was unable to think of a single thing to say. Instead, she just went on staring at him, horrified. Not yet, something in her brain was wailing. I'm not ready. Not *yet*.

Her reaction surprised him, she saw. One dark eyebrow rose.

'I startled you. You must have been a long way away.'

Oh, she was, she was. Nine years and a whole ocean away. Impossible to say that, of course. Engage brain, Rachel, she told herself furiously. Engage brain. Or this will go out of control before you've even said hello.

Years of professional negotiations came to her aid at last. The unforgotten past receded, at least for the moment.

She swallowed and said, 'Hello, Mr di Stefano.' It came out a lot huskier than she'd expected but at least it did not sound as if all she wanted to do was run away from him and hide.

He laughed aloud then. 'That sounds very formal.'

She gave him a quick, meaningless smile. 'That's the English for you.'

He smiled back. It was slow and sexy and made his eyes crinkle at the corners as if he was used to staring into the sun. He was not as tanned as she remembered, but the muscles were still as lithe under the city suit— and the laughter as wicked.

'Now, I've always found English formality to be a bit of a myth,' he said easily.

Oh, have you? she thought. Now that she had brought herself back under control she had time to observe him more dispassionately. She disliked what she saw amazingly. Confident, good-looking, intelligent. The things that her stepmother had gloated over all those years ago were still true. Even more so, if you could judge from one quick, resentful look. The charm was still there too— and he knew it. He was even waiting for her to respond to it. Rachel realised it in gathering wrath.

She said smartly, 'I'm afraid I'm rather a formal person.'

Riccardo di Stefano's eyes narrowed. It looked as if he had just registered that there was a real person confronting him in the corridor, Rachel thought, pleased. Her satisfaction was short-lived.

'Have we met before?'

She could have kicked herself. Never start a fight unless you're prepared to finish it, she reminded herself grimly.

She said in her most colourless voice, 'I was away when you were here in September.'

He detected the evasion. Of course he would. He had built up a worldwide empire on management skills, which meant that he would have no problem at all in reading a minor employee's disaffection.

He did not look worried by her attitude. Why should he? His reputation said he had a flair for rooting out opposition at the heart. He would have detected that this minor employee would not present him with any problems he could not deal with. Just let him not detect as well how carefully she had orchestrated her leave in order to avoid his thrice-postponed visit, Rachel thought.

Before he could challenge her further she said, 'Were you looking for the boardroom? You should have turned right out of the lift, not left.'

He was looking at her intently. Before he could question her she said, 'Let me show you.'

For a moment he did not say anything. She could feel him weighing up her reaction, assessing its implications, even its possible effect. Oh, yes, you could see why he was head of a multinational, multi-business empire.

She could have kicked herself. She held her breath, not quite looking at him. But he decided it was not worth probing, in the end.

'Thank you,' he said easily. 'I'd appreciate that.'

She breathed again.

He fell into step beside her. He did not say anything further, but Rachel could feel his thoughtful gaze on her profile. She hoped she kept her expression neutral. By the time they reached the boardroom she felt as if the whole of that side of her face had been irradiated. Doing her best to ignore the feeling, she opened the door.

'Mr di Stefano,' she announced to the room.

It was not necessary. All the men there already knew who he was as well as she did, Rachel could see. And most of them were scared of him. She saw that too.

Well, at least she wasn't scared of him, she thought. Not now. Maybe once. Not any more. It was ironic. He had done his worst to a vulnerable adolescent and she had survived. There was nothing left to be afraid of.

Reminding herself that she was totally unafraid of Riccardo di Stefano was one thing. Meeting his eyes and retaining conviction was something else entirely. Prudently, Rachel kept her head turned away from that piercing gaze. Luckily it was not difficult.

It became obvious that Riccardo di Stefano had come to Bentley's that morning with one object and one only. He was pleasant enough about it but underneath the good manners he was not making much attempt to hide that steely purpose. Philip Jensen was chairing the meeting and managed to deflect four pointed questions.

Eventually Riccardo di Stefano changed tack. He stopped asking questions and interrupted Philip in mid-waffle.

'Frankly, it seems to us at Di Stefano that you've lost your way,' he said.

Philip Jensen was unused to direct confrontation.

'If we can just keep with the agenda...' he began fussily.

Riccardo di Stefano pushed the papers away from him.

'Forget the agenda. What's the point of talking about whether to go into Eastern Europe next year when the bank could collapse at any time?'

Rachel gasped. She was not alone. Riccardo di Stefano's eyes swept round the table.

'That sounds like surprise,' he mocked.

Philip recovered. 'Collapse? What are you talking about?'

'Your little adventures into the futures market. You've got enough risk on board to wipe out the bank.'

Philip forgot he was in awe of Riccardo di Stefano. He sat bolt upright and glared. 'That's a preposterous suggestion.'

'Is it?'

Riccardo nodded to a quiet man whom Rachel knew to be his company's London director and who was on the bank's board. The man produced a pile of printed sheets and began to pass them round. The result of Angela's photocopying, presumably. Could Mandy possibly be right about his intending to put in a bid for the whole bank, then?

Rachel looked at the sheets blankly. They were figures of some sort. She was too shaken to focus on precisely what they represented.

The quiet man said, 'I've been saying I wasn't happy with bank strategy for six months. After the last board meeting I was so worried that I talked to Riccardo. He had our research department do a full analysis. These are the results.'

Philip picked up the stapled sheets and flicked through them. Sitting next to him, Rachel saw that his hands were shaking. He was clearly having as much difficulty in focusing on the figures as she had.

He managed, though, and looked up sharply. His eyes went very small and sharp and the tremor in his hands intensified.

'Where did you get these figures?'

Riccardo shrugged. 'Market information and some in-depth deduction. Then the research department in New York did some modelling. This is the result.'

Philip was shaking with anger now. With more than anger—fury.

'You've been spying. This is market sensitive.'

Riccardo looked amused. 'No need to spy. It's all out there in the market if you go looking for it. With Sam on the board, I knew what to look for, of course.'

Philip stood up. 'This is intolerable.'

Riccardo stood up as well. He looked utterly relaxed. How well Rachel remembered that cool, relaxed manner. How well she remembered how effectively he could use it—and with what devastating results. She braced herself.

Riccardo drawled, 'I rather agree.'

Philip blinked. All Rachel's protective instincts urged her to take his shaking hand. She curbed them. It would do no good and Philip would not thank her for humiliating him in public. She looked down at her own copy of Riccardo's figures again.

Riccardo said, 'Face it, Philip. You've driven this bank into the ground. Mismanagement followed by panic. Speaking as a major shareholder, I've had enough.'

Rachel was probably the only person at the table who was not surprised. Even Riccardo's quiet colleague looked taken aback. A general spluttering of indignation and recriminations broke out. Riccardo sat down again, leaning back in his chair. He watched them all lazily.

Rachel lifted her eyes from the papers in front of her. Across the table Riccardo was the only one not trying to make himself heard in the hubbub. The only one apart from her, that was.

Suddenly something seemed to draw his attention to her. Seeing her silent, he raised his brows. Then he looked directly at her, straight in the eyes. Rachel felt as if she had touched a naked wire. She jolted back in her seat, breaking the eye contact feverishly. But she knew he was still looking at her.

Beside her Philip was roaring, 'Breach of confidence... Complain to the authorities... The bank will sue...'

Riccardo was unimpressed. His lip curled faintly. He said nothing. Suddenly Rachel could not bear it any more. She stood up. The move was so unexpected that it attracted everyone's attention.

If she had ever imagined a scenario like this she would have been alarmed at the thought of taking public initiative away from Philip. But she had never imagined it. And anyway there were older and far more serious things she had feared in her life than Philip Jensen's potentially wounded ego.

So she said levelly, 'Gentlemen, the main item on the agenda was future business strategy. My report is in your folder as item four. I suggest we break to consider Mr di Stefano's analysis. Then we can come back and discuss it. We can look at the strategy options once we've agreed where the bank is falling down now.'

She sat down. There was a murmur of assent.

Riccardo had gone very still. The long-fingered hand on the table was clenched tight. His eyes looked black with an odd blind look in them as if a ravine had suddenly opened in front of him.

His director sent him a quick, enquiring look. Riccardo ignored him.

'How long?' he said at last. He spoke directly to Rachel. His tone was sharper than any he had used so far.

Rachel looked unseeingly down at the papers. She had not the slightest idea. She took a blind stab at a time.

'Three hours.'

He looked incredulous. 'You'll have proposals in three hours?'

Rachel thought, I have proposals now. You're not the only one who knows something has got to be done about this place. But I need time to convince Philip.

She said calmly, 'I believe so.'

It seemed as if everyone in the room was holding his breath. At last Riccardo di Stefano nodded.

'OK. Same place.' He looked at his watch. 'Two-thirty.'

He stood up. Everyone else did the same. As if he were an emperor, thought Rachel. She was not even trying to curb her hostility now. But still she somehow found herself on her feet too. That infuriated her.

Across the room, Riccardo di Stefano looked at her. His dark eyes measured her as if he had only just become aware of her. She thought she saw faint contempt and put a hand to her loose hair self-consciously. His eyes narrowed. Something in that basilisk regard brought Rachel to attention as if she were facing a court martial.

'I look forward to your ideas,' he said softly.

Something light as a feather, deadly as a cobra, slid up the back of Rachel's neck. She managed not to shudder, but only just. Instead she gave him a bland smile.

'I hope to surprise you.'

He laughed aloud at that. 'I'm sure you do. But I have to warn you a lot of guys have tried.'

And failed, was the implication.

Rachel said, 'I like a challenge.'

Riccardo di Stefano stopped laughing. The look he gave her was pure speculation.

'So do I,' he said softly. 'So do I. Maybe we're both going to learn something from this.'

CHAPTER TWO

As THE door closed behind Riccardo di Stefano, Philip sank back in his seat. He looked ill, Rachel thought with compassion. Beads of sweat were etching out a mask on his face. She was not the only one to notice.

'Better let Rachel run with this one, Phil,' said Henry Ockenden, the head of lending.

Philip waved a hand vaguely. Rachel took this as agreement. It looked as if he was not going to need much convincing after all. She got up.

'I'll be in my office. I'll get briefing to you by two at the latest,' she said.

She gathered up her papers and went.

Mandy was at her desk in the outer office. She raised her eyebrows as Rachel steamed past.

'Fireworks?'

'As you predicted,' said Rachel.

'Di Stefano on the attack?'

'And then some,' said Rachel with feeling. 'Call the group; I want a meeting in twenty minutes. Everyone to have a copy of these.' She dumped di Stefano's papers on Mandy's desk.

Mandy picked them up and took them to the photocopier.

'Is di Stefano as gorgeous as they say?' she said, pressing buttons briskly.

The copier warmed into life.

'Worse,' said Rachel crisply.

She turned away. Mandy was too observant. Rachel did not want the other woman to detect that this was not the first time she had had the opportunity to observe at close quarters how gorgeous he was. Or that she would give anything not to remember how gorgeous.

Rachel gave an angry little sigh. Riccardo di Stefano had obviously had no trouble forgetting. So why couldn't she?

Mandy, at the photocopier, was not detecting anything, fortunately. She laughed. 'He looks a heartbreaker all right.'

Rachel stiffened imperceptibly. Not turning round, she said casually over her shoulder, 'I thought you hadn't met him.'

'No.' It was not hard to discern Mandy's regret at this fact. 'He had his mug shot in the papers yesterday. Taking Sandy Marquis out on the town.'

'Sandy Marquis?' The name was vaguely familiar. Then she remembered. 'The model, you mean? The redhead discovered teaching gym to schoolgirls?'

'That's the one.' Mandy looked at Rachel speculatively. 'He seems to go for redheads.'

'He goes for anything female that doesn't run too fast,' muttered Rachel unwarily.

Mandy's eyebrows flew up. This time she was detecting. And accurately.

'You know him,' she said on a note of discovery.

That's what comes of losing your cool, Rachel told herself, annoyed. Aloud she said repressively, 'We've met.'

'Wow.' Mandy was impressed. 'You've been clubbing on the quiet?'

'Of course not. Even if that was how I got my kicks, which it isn't, what time do I have to go clubbing? When I'm not working I'm trying to persuade two adolescents that school isn't all bad.'

Mandy chuckled. 'I don't see di Stefano at a PTA meeting,' she allowed. 'Where on earth did you meet him, for heaven's sake?'

Rachel grimaced. Take it lightly, she adjured herself. It was never important. Don't build it up into something it was not.

She shrugged. 'It was a long time ago. I shouldn't think he even remembers.'

And I'm going to do everything I can think of to stop him remembering, she resolved fiercely.

'Have you said anything to him?'

'*No.*' Rachel was unable to disguise her horror.

Mandy looked even more intrigued. Rachel realised she could be getting herself into exactly the kind of trouble she had hoped to avoid—the kind of trouble that slapped an ice-pack on the back of her neck and sent her normally logical mind into meltdown. She could trust Mandy, of course, but if she told her it was a secret Mandy would inevitably start to wonder what it was all about. It was only human nature. It was also horrifying.

I can't stand that sort of speculation, Rachel thought. How can I avoid thinking about him if every time I put my head out of my office my secretary's asking herself what Riccardo di Stefano was to me in my dark past?

She felt panic rise. It took all her self-control to quell it, to think of a plausible story. It was half the truth anyway.

'Look,' said Rachel, 'I'd be grateful if you didn't mention it. It was no big deal but I was very young.' She managed to sound rueful, even faintly embarrassed. She was impressed with herself. 'It wouldn't do my credibility much good to remind him. I don't want him thinking he's negotiating with a spotty teenager with no control over her temper.'

No hint of the inner panic. Well done, Rachel, she congratulated herself. Mandy was taking it at face value anyway.

'No control...' Mandy stared. 'You?'

'Youth,' said Rachel. She gave a very good shrug, quite as if she did not care. She even managed a light laugh.

That was not quite so convincing, evidently. At least, it did not convince Mandy. 'Did you have a crush on him?' she demanded.

'No,' said Rachel with unmistakable truth. In spite of her determination to stay cool, she could not repress a shudder.

Mandy was not just a colleague, she was a friend. She saw the shudder and drew her own conclusions.

'Well, if he hasn't remembered yet, he probably won't,' she said comfortingly. 'Not with Sandy Marquis to keep him happy.'

'I'm relying on it,' said Rachel. She went into her office. In the doorway she paused and looked back. 'Oh, we've got a deadline. Two o'clock with Mr Jensen. You'd better find out what the group want in their sandwiches.'

Mandy grimaced. 'Right you are. Action stations.' She was already on the telephone when Rachel closed the door.

The room was uncannily quiet without the hum of the photocopier. Rachel sank down behind her desk and stretched out her legs in front of her. They were trembling.

There was an unfamiliar tension between her shoulderblades. She bent her head forward and sideways and the tension eased. It did not go away entirely, though. If she was any judge, it was not going to go away until Riccardo di Stefano was safely back on his own side of the Atlantic.

'Blast,' she said.

She rubbed her hand across the back of her neck in an uncharacteristic gesture. The muscles felt like iron. Even as the thought crossed her mind, she remembered another time when she had done the same thing. Her hand fell.

Another time and a whole world away. She got up and went to the window. Outside the rain ran greyly down the window. But the world of her too vivid memory was drenched in sunshine.

Rachel tipped her head forward and rested her brow against the window-pane. How could she ever have thought she had forgotten?

She closed her eyes and let the memories flood back.

She had never wanted to go. She had tried so hard not to. But she had been eighteen and the opposition had all been over twenty-one and had had the big guns.

'It will be the holiday of a lifetime,' her father had said heartily. Too heartily. Rachel had not noticed that at the time, of course. 'You've been tying yourself to your books too much. Now the exams are over you deserve a really good time. Judy and I both want you to go.'

And that had been the first objection. Rachel had never warmed to her father's second wife. Judy felt the same, she'd been sure. Most of the time they'd been polite to each other but that was as far as it had gone. Rachel had frankly been appalled at the idea of going off on a Caribbean holiday with her stepmother for company.

She had not said that to her father, of course. And what she had said had only caused him to persuade harder.

'Judy needs a holiday as much as you do. It's been a tough year, with the takeover and everything. She needs to get away from it all. Sun, sea and a bit of exotic night-life.' He laughed. 'Do you both good.'

Rachel said, 'Exotic night-life doesn't sound like me, Dad.'

But he was not to be deflected. 'Nonsense. All girls of your age want to spread their wings a bit.'

Presumably Judy had told him that. Presumably she had also convinced him that she and Rachel were virtual contemporaries and could not be better friends. None of Rachel's protests had any effect.

'It's very good of Judy to suggest it,' her father said in the end.

His tone had stopped being hearty. Rachel recognised an order when she heard it. He might just as well have said she did not have a choice.

'She's been invited to stay with some very old friends. They have taken a house in the Caribbean. Film-star luxury, I'm told. Judy needn't take you along, you know. Since she's offered, you owe it to all of us to accept gracefully.'

So she went. Later it occurred to her to wonder whether her father was already suspecting his young wife's restlessness. Maybe he'd sent Rachel along to act as some sort of chaperon. Or even as a substitute for conscience. If he had, he had been singularly out of luck, she thought now.

She had not suspected any such thing at the time, of course. To be honest, Rachel had not seen much of her father or Judy, particularly over the last year when her father's company had got into difficulties. Rachel herself had been working furiously hard to get into university. She and her father had met occasionally over the coffee-pot in the small hours. They'd exchanged tired quips. But they had not really talked since he'd married Judy.

So, if there were strains in the marriage, at that time Rachel had not known it. She'd just known she did not like Judy, and she had not been able to imagine why her stepmother would want to take her on holiday.

It had been some time before she'd found out why, but she had. By that time she'd no longer cared. She'd had her own hurt and her own guilt by then. By that time she'd no longer cared about anything except getting away and never seeing any of the inhabitants of the Villa Azul ever again.

Rachel opened her eyes and stared blindly at the London rain. In all the three weeks she had spent at the Villa Azul, it had never rained once, she remembered. She would wake up in the huge colonial bed to a sound like rain, but when she'd rushed to the window it had been to find that the sound was only the wind through the palm trees. She had been so homesick. So hungry for familiar sights and sounds. So alone.

Open-eyed, she stared out at the rain. Alone! She gave a harsh laugh that contained no amusement at all. Oh, she had been alone all right. Until that last night, when she had learned, briefly and unforgettably, that there were worse things than being alone—and that the worst loneliness of all was when you could not reach the person you were with. She felt sick, remembering.

But there was nothing else for it. Now she had started, the whole thing was coming back in cruel Technicolor.

The first time she'd met Riccardo di Stefano she had almost run away. He had been like an alien from another galaxy. Well, they all had been, at the Villa Azul. By that time Rachel had learned to expect every new acquaintance to possess a degree of sophistication she knew she could not deal with. By the time he arrived, Riccardo di Stefano was exactly what she was expecting.

Tall and slim, he arrived in the Caribbean with an all-year-round tan and the inscrutable dark glasses to go with it. His hair was so dark that it looked blue in the glare of the midday sun. He was wearing piratical cut-offs that could have belonged to the ragged urchins in the town, had it not been for the indiscreet designer label at the back of the belt.

He was not bothering with a shirt that day and even to Rachel's jaundiced eye its absence revealed muscles that could only be called impressive. He moved lazily, gracefully, as if he knew every eye was on him and did not give a damn. Rachel loathed him on sight.

The Villa Azul loved him. It was only to be expected.

But by that time she was loathing the Villa Azul and all its inhabitants with a ferocity that she would never have thought possible. It could not have been further away from the relaxing holiday her father had fondly described. There was no possibility of relaxing. Rachel had never felt more on edge in all her eighteen years.

One thing her father had been right about was the luxury, though. Rachel had never seen anything like it. The house party seemed to drink champagne at all hours, change their designer outfits three times a day and have personal trainers and hairdressers in constant attendance.

In fact, at first she thought Riccardo di Stefano was a new fitness expert. Only, then he took off the arrogant shades to reveal even more arrogant eyes. Rachel revised her opinion rapidly.

Slowly he surveyed the company scattered round the pool and the exotic gardens. His expression announced

that he was supremely bored. None of the tennis pro-
fessionals and expert scuba-divers would have allowed
themselves to look like that. It would have cost them
their job. It did not make Rachel like him any better.

And then their eyes met.

It was oddly shocking. Even on edge as she was,
Rachel felt her inner tension go up a couple of notches.
She stepped back as if she had walked too close to a
fire.

The stranger in the designer rags looked her up and
down. Rachel had just come up from the beach to collect
some fruit for her lunch. She had not bothered with a
wrap because she did not intend to stay. She was going
to go back to the beach and carry on reading in the shade
of a coconut palm. Indeed, she was still marking the
place in her book with one finger.

So all she was wearing was a dark one-piece bathing
suit. By the standards of the Villa Azul it was modest
to the point of puritanism. But, under that cool inspection, Rachel felt that she might as well have been
naked. Her face flamed.

Even across the width of the flamboyant garden, the
pirate recognised her reaction. His eyebrows rose. He
was clearly amused. Rachel blushed harder, and hated
him for it.

Nobody else paid any attention at all. At least, not to
her. That was nothing unusual. The sophisticated house
party had been bewildered by her arrival. Since then,
they had done their best to ignore her. Because, of
course, Judy had dumped her the moment they'd got to
the estate.

'This is Bill's daughter,' she had said, waving a hand
in Rachel's general direction.

After that she'd stripped off and dived into the pool.
She had not exchanged more than a dozen words with
Rachel since. She had not even bothered to introduce
their host.

He was, Rachel discovered, Anders Lemarck and said
to be something in oil. The other guests were vague on

his profession but very precise on his wealth, which was described as serious. On their arrival, he'd considered Rachel appraisingly, decided she was not worth getting up for and raised a casual hand in her direction.

'Hi, Bill's daughter.'

After that he'd ignored her too. If it had not been for the friendly islanders who ran the Villa Azul, Rachel would not even have had anywhere to sleep.

'Part of my education,' the eighteen-year-old Rachel had told herself. 'Nobody said education had to be pleasant.'

She'd established a routine of swimming and reading, keeping out of the way of the main party as much as she could. Until now it had worked fine. But the piratical stranger was something else.

In spite of herself she could not look away. She stared into the face she did not recognise and knew that she would recognise it anywhere in the world for evermore. It was not just the barbecue-deep tan and insolent eyes. It was something that seemed to look right into the heart of her and imprint his image on her very core. Rachel felt helpless all of a sudden.

If the other guests continued to ignore her, they were more than enthusiastic to greet him. Women in tiny, jewel-coloured bikinis converged on him; men turned from discussing stock-market prices to greet him. Even Anders got out of his hammock to shake his hand.

And I'm no better, standing here like a mesmerised rabbit, staring at him, thought Rachel. She was disgusted with herself. It was a real physical effort to break that eye contact. Even across the garden she could feel his resistance. But she did it.

She turned away and made for the terrace where the luxurious cold lunch was set out. These days, Rachel had learned to mingle with the sophisticated diners with reasonable confidence.

She was bending all her attention on a dish of exotic fruits, when she felt a butterfly touch against her bare arm. She brushed it away absently. Warm fingers caught and held her own.

Rachel gave a thoroughly unsophisticated squeak and let go of her plate. The pirate caught it neatly, one-handed.

'Don't tell me—you're the discus professional.' His voice was as casual as his appearance. Casual and low and horribly sexy.

He returned the plate to her with an enigmatic smile. Rachel swallowed hard. This was where that education proved its usefulness. She tried to remember all that the holiday had taught her about dealing with these people.

'Thank you,' she said, clutching at the plate. It tilted dangerously and half a mango fell off it. He caught that too.

'Not the discus,' he said thoughtfully. 'Maybe ping-pong?'

Rachel was embarrassed. That education did not seem to have stuck after all.

Annoyed with herself, she said curtly, 'Sorry, no,' and held out her hand for the fruit.

He turned it over with a grimace. 'Is this all you're eating?'

'I like fruit in the middle of the day.' Why did she sound so defensive?

His eyes crinkled at the corners. With half the garden between them she had thought his eyes were dark. Now she saw that they were a swirl of curious, complicated mineral colours, flecked with green. They were also oddly weary.

She thought suddenly, He looks as if he's seen every-thing in the world. And nothing matters to him any more.

She gave herself a quick shake. This was silly, melo-dramatic. He was a stranger. And not a very kind stranger, from the expression in those eyes. She did not think he would be kind if he knew what she was thinking about him, anyway.

He looked round at the little groups of people sitting under the trees.

'Who are you with?'

Rachel almost jumped. 'What?' Then she realised
what he meant. 'Oh. I'm not. I mean—'

He looked surprised, his brows rising interrogatively.
'You don't eat with the guests?'

'No,' she admitted. It felt like owning up to her lack
of sophistication all over again. She looked away.

He buffed his knuckles against the top of her arm.

'No need to look like that. So where do you take your
plunder?'

She looked up at that, laughing in quick surprise. At
once his eyes narrowed, became intent. Rachel saw that
the hand holding the mango clenched. Then slowly, as
if in an act of will, he relaxed his fingers and gave her
a slow, lazy smile.

'Well? Do you climb a tree, or what?' The laughing
voice said he shared her amusement.

'I've got a beach,' Rachel admitted. Laughter always
warmed her. The trouble was—and she had not learned
enough yet to know how dangerous this was—it also took
her off her guard.

'Really? A whole beach?'

'Well, no one else seems to use it.'

The pirate looked over his shoulder at the party again.
He shrugged.

'Surprise me,' he said cynically. 'Real sand, real
seaweed?' He shook his head. 'Messy.'

Rachel chuckled.

For a moment those strange eyes widened. Then he
seemed to shake himself. He looked down at the mango
he was still holding. It was looking distinctly the worse
for wear.

'You can't eat that.' He summoned one of the house
staff by some magic semaphore which Rachel was not
quick enough to catch. As the man appeared at his elbow,
he said, 'Take this away, will you? And bring some food
down to—' He broke off and turned compelling eyes on
Rachel. 'Where is this magic beach of yours?'

It was at the far end of the estate, outside the cabin she had been allotted by the staff. There was no point in trying to hide the location. This was the servant who had shown her to her room three days ago. The man nodded.

'Coconut Beach. I know. Gladly, sir.'

The pirate took the plate out of her suddenly nerveless fingers. 'You won't need that. Ben's a professional. He'll bring everything we need for a beach picnic, won't you, Ben?'

'I will, sir.'

Rachel did not at all like the look they exchanged. It was not far short of a grin. She suspected masculine conspiracy. It annoyed her. Worse, it made her uneasy.

But she could hardly prohibit one of Anders' guests from visiting to one of Anders' private beaches.

She said, 'Maybe I won't have anything to eat, after all. It's hot.'

'Plenty of shade on Coconut Beach,' Ben said, thereby confirming Rachel's suspicions about masculine solidarity.

The pirate chuckled. 'Lots of ice in that picnic, Ben. Plenty of nice ice-cold drinks. Oh, and the lady likes fruit.'

The man nodded. 'Leave it to me.'

He went. Rachel found she had an arm round her shoulders. It was warm and sinewy and it felt like iron. Her heart began to slam uncomfortably. She made a move to draw away and the arm tightened as she had somehow known it would. It set her very slightly off balance, so that she had to lean against him.

She looked up, uncertain. He was smiling down straight into her eyes. His expression made her head swim.

'And now take me to the seaweed.'

He took her down the shallow steps of the terrace into the midday glare. Even in her confusion, Rachel was aware of the eyes watching them. For days her fellow guests had seemed barely aware of her existence. Now she felt as if she were in a spotlight.

The pirate seemed unaware. Or, if he was aware of it, he did not care. Still with that long arm round her, he skirted the pool area, with its spectacular apricot-veined marble, and swept her off into the shade of the casuarina trees.

He let her go then. It was not practical to walk along the uneven, sandy path side by side. But he did not stop touching her. The path through the casuarinas was dotted with fallen vegetation—things like cones and scaly brown twigs. He put out a hand to help her skirt them. He brushed away the feathery branches that drooped over the path, holding them back for her to pass. Once or twice, perhaps by accident, his hand brushed her loose hair.

It was flattering. It was also slightly alarming. Rachel ducked her head and made for the beach without daring to meet his eyes again.

They came out through a grove of trees whose name she did not know. They were slim-trunked and fanned out to make a loose canopy overhead. The sun made a sharply etched lace pattern of shadows beneath.

'We could sit here. In the shade,' said Rachel, holding back a little.

In the garden her swimsuit had felt modest until he'd looked at her. Out here, with no companion but the ocean and the pirate, she suddenly needed the covering of shadows.

He shook his head.

'No, we can't.'

'But I'd rather.' Her embarrassment felt like panic. Her voice came out too high, too defensive. 'I can't take too much sun. My skin—'

He looked at her. It was like a caress. It silenced her. The sexy smile grew.

'Believe me, your skin would not like sitting under manchineel trees.'

'What?'

He put a hand against one of the slim branches. It was a large hand, long-fingered and brown as a nut. For no reason she could think of, Rachel's mouth dried.

'Manchineel,' he said. 'Poison apple. Didn't anyone warn you?'

Rachel shook her head. 'What's to warn?'

He frowned. 'Well, the fruit's poisonous, but you probably would not eat that. The leaves give off a sticky sap like lime trees. It's not exactly poisonous but it can irritate the skin. Some people react badly. There have been nasty cases of blistering. The bad thing is to be under the trees when it rains. The rain washes the sap off the leaves onto the people taking shelter beneath.'

'Oh.' Rachel looked at the beach, powder-white in a sunlight so intense that it seemed to hum. The sky was so pale that it was hardly blue. There was not a cloud in sight. She put her head on one side. 'An immediate danger, do you think?'

He stopped frowning and gave a bark of laughter. 'Maybe not today.'

'I'll bear it in mind for the next time it rains.'

'Bear it in mind for the next time you look at your contract,' he said cynically. 'Suing Anders can be lucrative.'

Rachel stared. 'My contract?'

'Working conditions are not supposed to include poisonous trees. Unreasonable hazard, if you were not warned.'

'Working conditions?'

But he was not listening to her. He was running across the baking sand to the shade of the coconut palms. He looked fit and free and utterly at one with the wild landscape. Rachel followed more slowly.

So he had not realised she was a guest. In fact he had made exactly the same mistake about her as she had about him, when she'd first seen him. She thought about the other guests, their casual acceptance of every luxury, their brittle laughter and their dark, dark tans. He had recognised at once that she was a misfit. It was not really surprising, she thought wryly.

By the time she reached the tree he had found her sunblock and towel. He shook the towel free of sand and spread it for her ceremoniously. Rachel laughed and sat down. But the misunderstanding still worried her.

She said, 'Look, I know I don't fit in here—'

He interrupted. 'Why should you? You're twenty years younger than most of them.'

It was closer to thirty years, if she were honest. Most of the house guests were Anders' contemporaries.

'That's not the point.'

He dropped down beside her and Rachel fell abruptly silent. She found quite suddenly that she could not remember what she had been going to say. The pirate sent her an amused, comprehending glance.

'Oh, but it is. You're not here to fit in. You're here to help them convince themselves they're having a good time.' The cynicism was harsh.

Rachel shifted uncomfortably.

'I'm not—'

'Yes, you are.'

He stretched out, propping himself on one elbow, and looked at her. His eyes were not unkind but they had a remote expression. Once again Rachel had the overwhelming impression of weariness.

'What do you think you're here for? To run aerobics sessions? Guide them round the reef?'

She opened her lips to correct him but he waved the suggestion away before she could speak.

'It doesn't matter what it says in the contract. Your real job here is to be their audience.'

'What?'

'Such an innocent.' He sounded almost sad.

Unexpectedly he cupped her face. It was a tender gesture, quite without sexual intent. But it set something fluttering under Rachel's breastbone that she had never been aware of before. She drew back instinctively. His hand fell.

She rushed into speech, the words tumbling out, only half-aware of what she was saying. More aware of the small reverberations she could still feel in every nerve and muscle. Aware of the need to hide that schoolgirl vulnerability to his fleeting gesture.

'You don't understand. It's not like that at all. They don't want me as an audience. They don't want me at all. I should never have come. The way they look at me.'

He said quietly, 'You're talking about envy.'

Rachel shook her head violently.

'No, I'm not. You haven't seen it.' She remembered last night's barbecue, the way people's eyes had glazed over as she'd approached. 'It's as if I'm spoiling things somehow. Like I'm an alien or something—some creature that's put a tentacle out of the sea and pulled itself up the beach to spoil the party.'

There was a little silence. Rachel realised she was shaking.

At last he said slowly, 'Spoil the party?'

She made a helpless gesture. 'I know it must sound stupid.'

'No.' He sat up, propping himself against the bark of the coconut palm. 'No, it sounds very lifelike.' She felt his reflective gaze on her face. 'They really didn't know what they were getting in you, did they?'

Before she could answer there were footsteps behind them. The manservant appeared at the top of the slope, bearing a rush basket.

The pirate looked up.

'Our picnic,' he said, amused.

He got lazily to his feet and went to receive it. He exchanged words with the man which Rachel could not catch. Then he brought the basket back to the shade of the tree.

'He'll pick it up later. All we have to do is eat, drink and enjoy ourselves.' He looked at the pale crescent of sand and gave the first unshadowed smile she had seen from him. 'Shouldn't be too tough.'

It was not. They swam, then talked while Rachel un-packed the basket, finding delicacies wrapped in foil and cool-boxes. There was flaked crab in a spice that burnt the tongue, barbecued prawns soaked in lime, wonderful crisp bread, a cornucopia of exotic fruits, and wine—wine such as she had never imagined, sharp and sweet at the same time, the bottle icy cool in its astronaut suit.

The pirate did not eat much, she saw, though he watched her appreciation with lazy amusement.

'It's wonderful,' she sighed at last, licking mango juice from her fingers.

He was propped against the tree.

'You like your pleasures simple.'

'Simple...' She stared. Then, seeing he meant it, she burst out laughing. 'And what would you call luxury?'

He was watching her with an odd, quizzical expression. He shrugged at her question.

'Oh, something with linen tablecloths and at least three Michelin stars. You'd have to wear diamonds.'

Rachel choked. 'I almost never wear my diamonds to swim,' she said gravely.

His eyes crinkled at the corners. 'Why is that?'

'It attracts the sharks. Or so they tell me.'

For a moment the strong face tightened. 'I've heard that too.'

Rachel looked at him. He had been a friendly, easy companion over lunch. So why was she reluctant to ask him about himself? He was self-evidently not the usual type of visitor to the Villa Azul, in spite of his familiarity with the names of the staff and the quality of the company. What was more, he had elected to spend half the day in her company. Her curiosity was perfectly understandable. Yet she sensed a reserve in him which would not permit invasion. And she did not think he would be kind if she intruded too far.

So she did not ask him who he was and what he was doing as Anders' guest. Instead she said carefully, 'Meet a lot of sharks, do you?'

His expression was inscrutable. 'My share.'

Rachel looked away from him. They were facing a view of breathtaking beauty over the pale beach to the Caribbean Sea. In the sun it looked like a cloth of silver. The distant islands could have been painted on silk, as insubstantial as dreams.

She said softly, 'Well, there are none here.'

There was a pause. He neither moved nor spoke. All she could hear was the steady lull of the waves against the shore and the cicadas in the trees behind them. Then he gave a long sigh.

He said slowly, as if something new had occurred to him and he was examining it, 'You could just be right.'

He stretched. Out of the corner of her eye Rachel saw him move. Instinctively she tensed. Something in her had been waiting for him to make a move in her direction ever since she'd first set eyes on him. She had been aware of it, increasingly, all during the afternoon. It was exciting, but it troubled her all the same. She did not know what she was going to do about it.

But her wariness was unnecessary. He was only lowering himself to lie full-length under the palm. He crossed his arms behind his head and tipped his head back. He closed his eyes and made a noise indicative of total satisfaction.

His lips barely moving, he said, 'Wake me up when it gets dark.'

CHAPTER THREE

RACHEL spent the next three hours swimming and sunbathing and reading her novel. The pirate slept deeply
beside her. At first she was disconcerted, even slightly
piqued. But then she remembered the terrible weariness
she had sensed and kept herself as quiet as a mouse in
order not to disturb his rest.

Eventually he stirred. Rachel put down her book and
looked at him. His eyes opened, drifted shut, stayed
closed for a moment. Then they flew wide open, a
startled expression in their depths.

'What—?'

Rachel laughed down at him gently. 'You were tired.
You ate. You slept.'

His eyes flickered and went dark. His expression
became unreadable. He continued to look up at her.
Rachel shifted a little, suddenly uncomfortable under
that unblinking stare. She tore her eyes away and made
a great business of tidying up the last of their picnic.
She even tried a little mockery to ease that sudden
tension.

'You don't snore.'

He still watched her. For a moment she thought he
was not going to reply.

Then he said idly, 'You reassure me.'

Still not looking at him, she wrapped glasses in the
napkins Ben had provided and stowed them carefully.
A thought occurred to her. She gestured to the picnic
basket. 'Would you like something?'

'Well . . .' His voice became a drawl. 'Maybe I would,
at that.'

Rachel was surprised but she peered inside the basket,
inspecting the remains.

44

'Cheese, breadfruit, pineapple— *Oh!*'

He had reached out a lazy hand and pulled at her shoulder. Not expecting it, Rachel fell back onto the sand in a tumble of flying hair. She was twisting her head, brushing hair from her eyes and mouth when the sky above her went dark.

'Pass on the pineapple,' said the pirate, leaning over her. He was amused. He bent forward.

She had been half braced for it all day but now that it was happening it came at her out of the blue. Really, she had the sophistication of a six-year-old, Rachel castigated herself. What was more, now the moment had arrived, she had not the faintest idea what to do about it.

'Oh, Lord,' said Rachel, shutting her eyes.

It was not a demanding kiss. He feathered his mouth over her lips, her brow, her eyelids. He took his time and seemed to enjoy it. Rachel thought she could feel him smiling. She swallowed and tried to relax.

He made a small sound of satisfaction and turned her head so that he could kiss the soft, vulnerable place below her ear. Rachel quivered. Suddenly she did not have to try any more. She was relaxing spontaneously. Her limbs felt as if they were melting, moulding themselves round him. She felt lazy, luxuriously alive to her fingertips.

She thought of the boys she had kissed or wanted to kiss at the occasional party she'd got to in London. It had never felt like this. She was not quite sure where the difference lay but she knew it had felt a world away from this. In London she had felt hot and anxious, terrified— of doing the wrong thing, of being laughed at, of being hurt.

If she was terrified now, thought Rachel dimly, it was not of anything the pirate might do. It was of the way he was making her feel.

He kissed her jaw, so lightly that it felt as if he did no more than breathe on her. Unbidden, Rachel's body jackknifed into an arch. He gave a soft laugh, his hands gentling her down again onto the sand. He slipped the straps of her swimsuit away so that he could kiss her warm bared shoulders.

Her eyes drifted half-shut. She was breathing rapidly. Her head tipped back in an agony of expectation. At last—at *last*—he found her mouth. This time his kiss was shockingly far from gentle.

So far that, in spite of her own body's hunger, Rachel was frightened. Her muscles locked, quite beyond her control. She felt suffocated. She tried to turn her head away.

For a moment he would not let her. His body was fierce on hers. Then, abruptly, he let her go and swung away from her.

Rachel lay there for a moment, fighting for breath. Beside her, the pirate sat up and stared out to sea.

'Crossed wires, I think,' he said at last drily.

Rachel was embarrassed. That annoyed her.

'You mean because you jumped on me?' she snapped unfairly. 'Why on earth did you do that?'

He shrugged, looking bored. 'Jumped on you? It's called a kiss. You should know that by now, even if you don't use them. As for why... Because I wanted to. Don't you ever do things just because you want to?'

Rachel stared up at him, arrested. Her bad temper evaporated, taking embarrassment with it.

'No,' she said slowly, recognising the truth even as she said it.

He looked down at her then. The heavy eyebrows rose. 'You serious?'

She pushed herself away so that there was no chance of touching him and sat up. 'Yes.'

She pulled up the straps of her swimsuit, brushing the sand off her arms and shoulders. He watched her through narrowed eyes.

'You going to tell me why?'

'What?'

'Why you don't follow your instincts,' he said patiently.

Rachel shook her head. She felt odd. That must be why she'd told him the straight, unembroidered truth. Up till then she had not even recognised it herself.

She gave a short laugh. 'Oh, instincts. Something else I've heard about and don't use. As you must realise.'

She kept her head proudly high but she did not quite manage to meet his eyes. The pirate sat bolt upright. He looked at her broodingly.

Finally, he said ruefully, 'It looks like I've got more than I bargained for as well, doesn't it?' He put out a hand as if to touch her face and then changed his mind. 'Want to tell me about it?'

Rachel let out a breath she had not known she was holding.

'Not a lot to tell,' she said carefully. 'That's rather the point.'

She did meet his eyes then. He was taken aback but he did not pretend he did not understand.

'So why haven't those instincts of yours had an outing before? What have you been doing?' he said lightly. 'Living on a desert island? Hiding in a convent?'

Rachel gave a choke of laughter. 'Just about. Going to a girls' college and working for exams.'

'Ah. Working.' He nodded, as if he really did understand then. 'You can do too much of that.'

'All work and no play makes Jack a dull boy,' agreed Rachel. 'So my stepmother keeps telling me.'

At that he did touch her—not her face but her upper arm—running the back of his hand down her warm skin, almost as if he could not help himself.

'So you're at the Villa Azul to learn to play.'

'*No.*' Rachel sounded appalled.

He flung back his head and laughed.

She was confused, blushing. 'Oh, I didn't mean it like that. Not the way it sounded.'

'Yes, you did,' he contradicted her, still chuckling. 'Nothing wrong with that. They're not exactly role models, Anders and his cronies. I should have remembered that. Now, what you need is—'

But Rachel was not to hear what the pirate thought she needed. Ben had appeared, slithering down the slope to them.

'You finished, Mr Rick?' he asked.

The pirate hesitated. Then he shrugged and got to his feet.

'I guess so.' He looked down at Rachel. 'For the moment.'

The manservant gave him a quick look. He said without expression, 'Mr Lemarck been asking where you are.'

'I'll bet he has.'

'You want to talk to him, better be quick. Got a big party tonight. Guest's birthday.'

Rachel stood up too. She held out her hand to the pirate. 'Better be going, then. It takes everyone long enough to get ready for the small parties,' she said wryly.

He took her hand but he did not shake it. He held onto it. 'I guess you're right. I'll see you this evening.'

Ben's expression became wooden.

Rachel said hastily, 'I'm not sure. I've had a lot of sun today. Maybe I'll just—'

The hand holding hers tightened. 'I obviously didn't make myself clear,' said the pirate softly. 'Let me lay it on the line for you. I'll see you at the party. If I don't, I come get you. Your choice.'

Under the manservant's expressionless gaze, he pulled her towards him and gave her a brisk kiss. It was neither passionate nor seductive but it shocked Rachel to the core. It spoke of total possession.

Then he hoisted the picnic basket and set off up the sandy slope. Startled out of his perfect training, Ben exchanged one stunned look with Rachel and then dashed after him. Rachel could hear them arguing about who carried the basket until the engine of the shooting-brake started up.

She gathered up her towel and book. As soon as she was sure that the engine noise had died away and they were not coming back for any reason, she toiled up the

slope. The faint evening breeze was just beginning to
whip up from the sea but it was not because of that
warm current of air that she was trembling when she
reached her cabin. She closed the door and leaned against
it, trying to collect her wits.

The cabin was at the very far end of the Villa Azul's
grounds, half-hidden behind a hedge of bougainvillea
and a huge hibiscus bush. A pretty maid, about her own
age, came every day to change the linen. Apart from
that daily visit, Rachel had been left severely alone, with
her palm trees and her sea views. It had suited her very
well up to now. This evening, for the first time since
she'd arrived, Rachel would have given anything for the
company of one of her friends.

But there was no one to discuss the pirate's strange
behaviour, still less her own uncertain reaction to it. So
Rachel, being a practical girl, climbed out of her swimsuit
and into the shower. She was washing her salt-encrusted
hair for the second time when she heard the door rattle.

For a moment she froze. Then she heard her name
called. It was a woman's voice.

'I'm in the shower,' she called back.

'I'll wait.' It had to be Judy, thought Rachel in
surprise.

'Just let me rinse my hair and I'll be out.'

She did so and padded into the main room, wrapping
her hair turbanwise in one of the Villa Azul's daily clean
towels. She was swathed in another. Her stepmother was
sitting at the elegant dressing table, peering at herself in
the mirror. When Rachel came out of the bathroom, she
swung round.

'I've been swimming,' said Rachel, instantly defensive.

Judy looked resigned. But all she said was, 'I hope
you brought enough conditioner. Sea-water is terribly
drying.'

Rachel was even more surprised. Judy did not bother
herself with her stepdaughter's appearance even in
London. Here at the Villa Azul she had done her best
to ignore her existence.

Judy read her expression. Briefly, she looked un-comfortable. She started fiddling with the trinkets on the dressing table.

'You'll want to look your best tonight. It's going to be a big party.'

'Even bigger?' Rachel asked drily. She sat on the bed and curled her legs under her, watching her step-mother's reflection interestedly.

Judy ignored the barb, if she noticed it.

'Yes. Anders has got Corporal Lili to play. And the local steel band, of course. Some guitarist for later. Dinner is formal and then there'll be dancing on the lawn.' She drew a long breath and came to what was clearly the ultimate in these delights. 'Lots of Press, of course.'

She sent Rachel a quick look in the mirror and gave a little laugh. It sounded false.

'Of course, I know it's not your sort of thing. No disco or teenage yobs. But it will be a once-in-a-lifetime experience for you. You can't pass it up. Not a party like this.'

Rachel's eyes narrowed. She knew quite well that she could not pass it up. Not unless she wanted a pirate to come looking for her in her private quarters—with consequences she was certain that she was not equipped to deal with. But she did not tell Judy that. She was wondering exactly why Judy wanted her there. She was prepared to be devious to find out.

So she stretched and said, 'Oh, I don't know.' She did not try telling Judy she had had too much swimming and sun. She gave Judy an excuse she would believe. 'I haven't got the clothes for a jet-set party.'

Judy stopped playing with the dressing-table trinkets and swung round.

'I know,' she said eagerly. 'I thought you'd want to borrow. I brought a couple of things over.'

She nodded at the wardrobe and Rachel realised the door was supporting hangers draped in silk and glitter that had not been there before. She considered them for a moment. Then she shrugged.

'I'm not a sequin sort of girl.'

Judy's face darkened. 'Don't be difficult, Rachel. They're both designer names.'

Rachel plumped up the pillows and settled down into them. She was enjoying herself.

'Maybe I'm not a designer girl either.'

Judy's fists clenched. But she knew that Rachel was winding her up. 'If you want to turn up in your jeans, that's up to you.'

Rachel smiled. 'I don't want to turn up at all,' she pointed out.

Judy looked alarmed. 'You've got to.' Her voice rose unattractively. She brought it under control. 'You're as much a guest here as I am. It would be unforgivable if you cut Anders' big party.' Her eyes hard, she said with deliberation, 'People would talk.'

Rachel raised her brows.

Judy drew a deep breath. 'Look, it's my birthday.'

For some reason it sounded like a confession. Rachel stared uncomprehending. Then, suddenly, she saw.

'It's not Anders' big party at all, is it?' she said slowly. 'It's yours.'

Judy looked away, shrugging.

Abruptly Rachel stopped enjoying herself. She sat up. 'What's going on, Judy?'

Judy looked back at her. Her eyes were bitter, though her painted lips stretched into a smile. 'Oh, come *on*, Rachel.'

All Rachel's suspicions suddenly became a certainty. She felt slightly sick.

'You're having an affair with Anders, aren't you? You're not even trying to be discreet about it.'

'You noticed!' Judy mocked.

'So why on earth did you want me along?' Rachel cried.

'Why on earth do you think? To keep your father quiet, of course.'

Rachel's lip curled. 'You mean you still have a use for him?'

To her surprise, Judy did not lash out at that. Instead her eyes fell. For a moment, for all the exquisite make-up and the elegant clothes, she looked haunted and almost old.

'You don't know what it's like,' she said, half to herself. 'Wanting him so much. Never *knowing...*'

'Don't!' Rachel's voice was harsh. In spite of herself, she was curious. 'Why didn't you marry him?'

Judy's incredulous look was answer enough.

'So you still need my father to pay your bills.'

'No. Well, not only that. I need—a place in the world. I'm not like you. You'll have your degree, a career. I haven't got any of that. If I'm not a wife, I'm nothing.'

Rachel's laugh hurt. 'And I thought you were a rich man's mistress.'

Judy shook her head. Her chandelier earrings jingled. 'Holiday fantasy, darling. Real life is back in London, waiting. At least—'

'As long as you don't burn your boats out here,' interpreted Rachel.

Judy was smiling again. 'Of course. Which is why you must turn up this evening. Too many gossip columnists not to. What do you think the papers will say if my step-daughter isn't there? Do you want your father to read *that*?'

There was a long silence.

'You mean you want me there for the press call,' Rachel said at last.

Judy laughed. 'If that's the way you want to put it...' She went over to the wardrobe and took down the hangers. 'Try them on. You've never worn anything like this. Come on, Rachel; you're a woman, aren't you? Live a little.'

Rachel just looked at her. Judy lost her temper. She flung the clothes across the end of the bed.

'Please yourself. And if your father doesn't like the gossip—' her tone was suddenly malicious '—you can tell him exactly why you fell down as a security guard.'

She stamped out. Rachel felt sick and rather dirty. She went and stood under the shower again until she felt better. When she came out, her hair conditioned and smelling of orange-flowers, the abrupt Caribbean night had fallen.

There was a knock on the door. Warily Rachel went to answer it. But it was only Stephanie, one of the maids.

'Oh, it's you. Come in.'

Stephanie smiled. 'I came to see if you wanted any help.'

Rachel was suspicious. 'Did my stepmother send you?'

Stephanie looked surprised. 'Nobody sent me. All the ladies want their dresses pressed, taken up, taken down. I thought you might too. What are you wearing?'

Rachel looked with dislike at the multicoloured heap on the end of the bed.

'Oh,' said Stephanie, intrigued.

'Borrowed. From God knows who. Not Judy—she's the wrong size. I'm assured they're *very* expensive.' Even to herself she sounded savage.

'Oh,' said Stephanie again in tones of complete understanding. 'Perhaps you would prefer something else?'

'I'd prefer not to go at all.'

But if I don't, she thought, and the papers pick it up as Judy thinks they will, Daddy will read it and be hurt. I can't do that to him. Not after the year he's had. Oh, why did he send me along? It's crazy, expecting me to chaperon a woman twice my age.

'Then why not stay here?'

'Family obligations,' Rachel said with a ghost of a smile.

'Ah.' Diplomatically Stephanie did not comment further. Instead she was rummaging at the bottom of the chest of drawers. A strong smell of lavender filled the room. Stephanie gave a cry of triumph and stood up with her prize. Rachel stared.

'What's that? It looks like a counterpane.'

Stephanie threw the material away from her. It billowed up and floated down onto the bed, in shades of smoke and copper and gold.

'A sarong,' she explained.

Rachel picked up a corner. 'It still looks like a counterpane. What do you do with it?'

Stephanie showed her, whipping the fine stuff round her over her green-checked uniform and knotting it between her breasts. Rachel regarded it dubiously. Without the green-checked dress, she thought, it was going to be terribly revealing. She said so.

Stephanie laughed and picked up the nearest hanger. She held the sequinned top against Rachel. It was evident that the neckline plunged dangerously low.

'I see what you mean,' Rachel admitted.

'You are not so pale any more. And if you put that wonderful hair on top like this...' Stephanie showed her in the mirror, warming to her theme. 'You need long earrings. Bangles. A gold chain or two.'

Rachel turned away from the sarong material, sighing. 'No jewellery. Sorry.'

Stephanie was not put out. 'I will borrow. You do not need anything valuable. Just the things that the ladies would wear to sit by the swimming pool. I will ask.'

And she was gone.

So an hour later Rachel pushed her way through the casuarina trees at the far end of the garden, feeling extraordinarily exposed and shy. The warm breeze touched her skin, reminding her constantly that her shoulders were bare. She wore long jet earrings, emphasising her pale throat and the soft tendrils of red-gold hair that escaped artlessly from Stephanie's inspired swirl.

But Stephanie had relented as far as further jewellery was concerned. Instead, Rachel had a golden trumpet of hibiscus in her hair and another at her waist. In the mirror she had looked like a stranger—a beautiful, exotic stranger with apprehensive eyes.

She stood for a moment in the shadow of the trees, watching the party. It was obviously as sophisticated as Judy had said it would be. She could not see her host or the chart-topping group he had hired but there was a fair crowd of expensively dressed people on the terrace and round the pool. Rachel noted white dinner jackets and jewel-coloured silks and shrank back into the grateful shade of the trees. She wished herself anywhere else in the world.

There was no sign of the pirate.

She drew a deep breath and made her way to the terrace. Above the background music, the cocktail party buzz and the clink of glasses, her ear caught snippets of conversation.

A long-legged blonde called Helen was saying, 'Sylvie's here.'

Her companion expressed surprise.

'She rang earlier,' Helen said. 'She's with the Lamberts. The yacht docked in St Lucia yesterday. So when she called Anders asked them to the party.' She added in a voice pregnant with meaning, 'She's bringing them over. And Riccardo.'

The companion was satisfactorily impressed. 'Riccardo di Stefano? I thought that was over.'

Helen giggled. 'So does he. So does everyone except poor Sylvie.'

Rachel turned away, wincing for the unknown Sylvie. But the next overheard gossip was even more unpalatable.

'Do you think she'll get him?' a grey-haired woman was saying. She wore a skintight coral dress with a neckline that plunged to her navel. Everything you could see, and you could see a lot, was as brown as a coconut.

'Judy? Get Anders? Shouldn't think so.'

Rachel stiffened and stopped strolling.

Someone else said, 'He didn't stop her marrying her dull Englishman. Don't see why he should bother now.'

Rachel stood as if turned to stone. Oh, Daddy, she thought. Poor, poor Daddy.

'So why is he giving a party like this for her?'

'Don't be silly darling,' said the grey-haired woman. 'Anders always gives a big party when he's at the Villa Azul. It's supposed to be fun but really he asks all the people he wants to do business with. Kent and I were asked months ago when he started negotiating for the Gregor field. Judy has just hijacked it, that's all. She's trying to manipulate him.'

'Then she's lost her touch,' said a short, dark-haired man indifferently. 'God, you women! Millionaires are dangerous to your health.'

How right you are, thought Rachel. Her skin crawled. A passing waiter held out a tray to her. She took one of the offered glasses, uncaring as to its contents, and took a great gulp.

It was champagne. Of course. Trying not to cough, Rachel turned away. She felt bitterly scornful of the whole party and everyone there.

Then, across the terrace, she saw her stepmother. After what she had just heard, she was almost sick. Hard-eyed, Rachel watched Judy's progress.

Her stepmother was certainly doing her best to act the hostess. She drifted from group to group, putting proprietorial hands on people's backs as she exchanged a few words, summoning waiters to top up emptying glasses, making sure she was seen doing just that. Judy might say she wanted to stay married, but she clearly wanted everyone to see her position at Anders' side more. Rachel's sympathy for her father turned into slow-burning rage.

Judy caught sight of her. She came over, her eyes sharp. The rage seemed to be mutual.

'What on earth are you wearing?'

Rachel did not answer. She was too angry. She folded her lips together tight in order not to say exactly what she was feeling.

Judy glared for a moment, then shrugged. 'Oh, well, at least it looks original, I suppose. Now, dinner—there's a table plan by the bar. I suggest you have a look.'

Rachel nodded.

Judy's voice hardened. 'And try to behave in a civilised fashion. All this glowering is very embarrassing. You're only making yourself look utterly naïve.'

Anders had appeared at the far end of the kidney-shaped pool, talking to knot of people. He looked serious and so did they. Rachel could well believe their conversation was pure business.

Judy caught sight of him. She took no more notice of Rachel. She picked up two glasses of champagne and went purposefully to his side. Rachel watched.

Judy was wearing tiger-striped chiffon and quantities of gold chains which chinked as she moved. Her eyelids, Rachel saw now in the light of the brilliant poolside torches, were as gold as her jewellery. She looked like a Hollywood pattern of a pagan princess. She gave Anders his champagne but she slipped her hand into the arm of another man in the group. Her eyes were challenging.

Her words floated up to Rachel. 'Oh, good. Another lovely eligible bachelor. I haven't seen you for ages, Ricky.'

The man she was standing next to looked down at her. He was tall and elegant in his dinner jacket but something in the gesture made him seem preoccupied. Another of Anders' business cronies pretending to be on holiday, Rachel thought, her lip curling.

Then he turned slightly and the harsh lights threw his profile into relief. Rachel received yet another shock— her worst yet. It was the pirate.

She stood mesmerised. Her hands slowly clenched on the terrace balustrade. It seemed impossible that he should not look up and see her, so intense was her gaze.

Someone else noticed.

'Who's that? Oh, di Stefano,' said the grey-haired woman on whom Rachel had eavesdropped earlier. 'Back from South America, then.' She leaned over the balustrade, peering. 'I heard he'd been ill. Doesn't look it, does he? Heck, he's a good-looking man.'

'Isn't he heaven?' said a girl who answered, to Rachel's surprise, to the name of Monkey. She added wistfully, 'Do you know him?'

Another woman laughed. 'I had a bijou flingette with him in Aspen last year. Heaven just about covers it. Trouble is, it never lasts with him.'

'All that turbulent Italian blood, darling,' said the grey-haired one. 'Can't expect it to last.'

'Italian? But surely...? He sounds American.'

'Fourth-generation New York but the family came from Genoa originally. Great-grandfather was a black sheep, though he made money fast enough. Riccardo always says he was thrown out for seducing the mayor's daughter.'

'It's in the genes, then,' sighed Monkey.

'That and the rest,' said the woman from Aspen. 'Everything he touches turns to gold.'

Rachel wanted to turn away, not to hear the cynical gossip. She had *liked* the pirate. Yet she had to listen.

'Slippery?' asked the grey-haired woman, unsurprised.

'As an eel, darling. Don't know why Sylvie doesn't face it. Like he says himself, he travels light.'

'And does he travel,' agreed the other. She turned to Rachel. 'Known him long?'

'What?' Rachel jumped at being directly addressed. She pulled herself together quickly. 'Oh, no. We've only just met. I didn't even know his name.'

The other women exchanged glances.

One of them said kindly enough, 'Di Stefano's a heartbreaker. He should leave a baby like you alone.'

Rachel flushed. 'He has. I mean, we only met. We just talked. I—'

I was going to meet him this evening. He was going to come and get me if I didn't come to the party. He slept beside me on my beach this afternoon. He kissed me; he teased me about my instincts. I thought he was *different*.

Well, of course, said a newly awakened, cynical voice in her head. He would not be much of a heartbreaker if he could not manage to convince a girl that he was different. Suddenly her anger took on a new focus, directed no longer at the Villa Azul sophisticates, no longer at Anders, not even at Judy in her predatory gold. Riccardo di Stefano, pirate heartbreaker and liar.

Oh, she would show him, Rachel vowed. She was trembling with outrage. She would make him sorry, as none of the other girls had ever managed to make him sorry. She would puncture that ego, tear off that charming, lying mask, make him *hurt* as he had hurt so many others. And then she would laugh.

CHAPTER FOUR

RICCARDO had said that, in Rachel, he had got more than he'd bargained for with her. He was going to find out how true that was, Rachel promised herself. But first she was going to have to make herself look like the rest of Anders' party people.

She retreated to one of the downstairs cloakrooms and considered the problem in the mirror. She was not alone. The sumptuous blonde called Helen was painting her sultry eyelids with a tiny brush. She ignored Rachel but when the door opened and Monkey came in she gave a little shriek of pleasure.

'Darling. Wondered if you'd be here.'

They air-kissed. Monkey sat down on a little dressing stool and began to make liberal use of the cosmetics set out there for the use of guests. They sat side by side, concentrating on composition.

'Have you seen who's here?' said the blonde, her mouth not moving as she drew a careful outline. 'Ricky.'

Monkey sent her a warning look in the mirror.

'Trust you, Helen. Yes, I've seen him in the distance. He's been spending time with—' She gave up on Rachel's name and nodded her head in her direction.

'Really?' The blonde removed the little brush carefully and turned incredulous eyes on Rachel. 'Have we met?'

'My stepmother is a friend of Anders,' Rachel said curtly.

'Oh.' Helen nodded, understanding perfectly. 'The college girl. You're staying here.'

Rachel nodded. She contemplated the cosmetics critically. Should she go for the natural look or go for the high glamour of Judy and Helen? With the paint-box before her the possibilities were infinite.

Helen was evidently still intrigued by her audience with the pirate. 'You've actually talked to Ricky di Stefano?'

You would think he was a rock star, Rachel thought contemptuously. She shrugged. 'A bit.'

There was a respectful silence.

'It must be because you're clever,' the blonde and sultry Helen said at last, plainly bewildered. 'He's supposed to be the most brilliant trader on Wall Street.'

'No, that's wrong, darling,' Monkey corrected her. 'Money is in the family.'

'Yes, but he quarrelled with his family. Never sees them. He made this million all by himself.'

Monkey looked suitably reverent.

'Could that be why everyone says he's so attractive?' Rachel wondered aloud.

She leaned forward, trying a purple-grey shadow on the corner of her eyelids. A glittery-eyed reflection looked back at her, cool and dangerous.

Helen gave her a dry look. 'Honey, if you don't know why Rick di Stefano's attractive, you're even younger than you look.'

Rachel looked down at the paint-box, willing herself not to blush. She swirled the brush around savagely in some gold-shot bronze shadow. 'He's hardly the most good-looking man around.'

'Oh, looks,' Monkey waved them aside. 'It's the way he makes you feel when he looks at you.' She gave a little shiver which strained the bikini-top to her vibrant dress almost to breaking-point. 'Mmm. All weak and wonderful.'

'He doesn't make me feel like that,' said Rachel defiantly.

The two women looked at each other and laughed. They went out.

Left alone, Rachel darkened her thick lashes, painted dramatic shadows about her madeira-wine eyes, and turned her mouth a luminous browny-gold. When she was satisfied, she stepped away from the mirror, fluffed up her hair and lowered the top of the sarong to a level that was just about decent.

'That will give Judy a run for her money,' she told her reflection with satisfaction.

She might not look like a Hollywood princess but she was young and she had been to enough parties to have learned a certain style. Judy, she resolved grimly, was not going to know what hit her. And nor were any of the rest of those cynical beauties.

And nor was Riccardo di Stefano. Her heart hurt when she thought about him. He had seemed so different. On the beach he had talked as if he and she were on the same side. It was an agony to find that they weren't. He was in the same team as Helen and Monkey and the whole crew of the Villa Azul. How he must have been laughing at her this afternoon.

Well, he was not going to laugh any more, Rachel vowed as she made her way to the pool area. The borrowed sarong clung to her legs as she walked. The night air was cool on her exposed shoulders. She felt like a war maiden, utterly ready to go into battle.

She did not look at Riccardo as she went up to the group.

'Good evening,' she said quietly.

Anders looked up. His surprise was almost comical as he took in her appearance. He pursed his lips in a soundless whistle.

'Hel*lo*, Rachel. Giving the party a chance?' He looked quickly at Judy, who was still clinging to Riccardo di Stefano's arm. 'You look good enough to eat. So when does the ice thaw, sweetheart?'

Judy let go of di Stefano's arm and gave a tinkling laugh. 'Or a refugee from *South Pacific*. Darling, did you think it was a fancy-dress party?'

Two hours ago, Rachel would have blushed and fled. Now, however, she was armoured by her anger—anger and a queer coldness, as if a limb had been amputated and she had not quite begun to feel the pain yet.

So she put a hand to the hibiscus flower in her hair and caressed it. It was an affected, even a flirtatious gesture. It was meant to be. Although she was not looking at him she could feel Riccardo staring at her.

'This, do you mean? I thought it would help me melt into the background,' Rachel said sweetly.

One of the men—not Riccardo di Stefano—laughed. Judy's face darkened.

Anders said quickly, 'I hope you won't, though. Not now you've made up your mind to join us at last.' He said to the others in explanation, 'Rachel has been very tired. We left her to recover in her own time. You will sympathise with that, Rick.'

Rachel did not understand that last remark, but she knew she had run out of excuses to ignore Riccardo di Stefano. Reluctantly, she turned. He was looking stunned. It pleased her. It was some balm to her sore heart.

Di Stefano said slowly, 'Rachel?'

'A relation of Judy's,' Anders said smoothly. He made the introductions swiftly. 'Letitia and Ronnie Lambert. Sylvie Ford. Piers Hilton-Dennis. Riccardo di Stefano.'

'We've met,' di Stefano said curtly, cutting over the polite murmurs of the others.

He did not look very pleased about it. The man who had threatened to come and get her if she did not turn up to the party seemed strangely unenthusiastic now that she was here as instructed, she thought. It turned the knife a little deeper in the wound.

Rachel pretended to study him from under mascaraed lashes. In fact she was startled by the alteration in him. It was not just that he had changed out of his cut-off jeans into the black-tie uniform of the businessman at play. With the dark jacket and trousers had come an indefinable air of authority. He looked older and far more tense, as if his patience was on a very short rein.

Rachel shrugged. It was nothing to do with her if he chose to behave like a chameleon. As long as he did not hurt her, it did not matter what he did. And it was up

to her to see that he did not hurt her, at least any more
than he had done already. She got back into her new
character and held out her hand, prettily.

'Yes, but we didn't introduce ourselves. Hello, Mr di
Stefano.' Her whole manner said that he was a generation ahead of her and she was a nicely behaved adolescent. That should get him on the raw, she thought.

His expression was unreadable. 'Hello, Rachel.'

He took her hand. But instead of shaking it he carried
it to his lips. It was not a conventional, polite brushing
of the air above her knuckles either, but a real kiss. It
was quite deliberate and it was not intended as a
compliment.

Her careful indifference turned to ashes. Rachel
jumped and snatched her hand away. She tried hard not
to blush. She was not sure she was successful.

Sylvie Ford looked at her narrowly. She was not un-
sympathetic, Rachel thought. It was an added humili-
ation.

Sylvie was a dark gamine beauty with lines round her
eyes which revealed that she was not as young as her
dress sense invited you to think. Or as carefree. Now
she took hold of Riccardo's arm.

'Have you been hiding behind dark glasses again,
darling? You know, it's really not fair, going around like
a prince in disguise.'

'On the contrary,' he said coolly, not taking his eyes
from Rachel's flustered face. 'If anyone was in disguise,
it was Rachel.'

Sylvie gave a little crow of laughter. She sounded
genuinely delighted.

'Then now you know what it's like. I hope it teaches
you a lesson.'

His eyes dropped to Rachel's painted and glowing
mouth.

'Do you know, I think it just might,' he drawled.

He lifted his eyes and met Rachel's. Startled, she recognised a rage as great as her own. Only, it was far better
controlled. She took a step backwards from pure instinct.

Riccardo di Stefano smiled. It was not a nice smile. And it was very clear whom it was aimed at. Somehow she had managed to turn Riccardo di Stefano into a personal enemy. It shook Rachel to the core. And, although she did not want to think about it now, beyond the shock there was a grief as great as for the loss of a friend.

She was not the only one disconcerted. There was a sharp little silence. Then three of the group started to talk at once.

'Time you looked at the seating plan,' Judy said sharply to Rachel.

At the same time, Sylvie said to Riccardo, 'Darling, we really ought to say hello to Marthe.'

With an apologetic smile at Anders, she began to draw him away. She looked like a small, determined tug towing a liner. Riccardo did not acknowledge anyone, even his host, by so much as a look. But at least he went. When he had gone there was a collective sigh of relief.

'That man gets more impossible every time,' muttered Hilton-Dennis.

Anders looked sharp and spiteful suddenly. 'If he weren't so damned successful, I wouldn't give him the time of day. But face it, Piers—we need men like that. The new generation.'

He glowered at di Stefano's departing figure. Nor was he alone, Rachel saw. From the way he and Sylvie were received, it seemed that the men were at least as resentful as they were admiring. By contrast, the women did not attempt to disguise the fascination he had for them. Which presumably made their escorts even more equivocal.

Not that Riccardo di Stefano noticed. In fact, he did not seem to be noticing anyone very much that night— not his host, not the gamine beauty on his arm, not anyone from the eager groups who greeted him. No one except Rachel.

He seemed as if he could not take his eyes off her. Every time she looked up, there he was, his narrowed gaze fixed on her, his face expressionless. Rachel stopped pretending to circulate and watched him.

He was neither the tallest nor the most handsome man there by any measure. But there was an indefinable presence about him, like an invisible cloak, which made people turn towards him as if they felt its touch. Was it something to do with the cool, commanding air he had? He was not handsome. He had heavy brows and high, haughty cheekbones that made him look hard and cold as an iceberg.

In fact this evening he was looking so cold that Rachel found it difficult to believe he was the same man who had kissed her on the beach. Yet this was the man that those women she had overheard knew, not the casual pirate.

Could they really find him attractive? she wondered, shivering. You could burn yourself on the ice in his eyes. Yet as he mingled with the party-goers women turned to him as if they needed something from him. Heaven preserve me from ever needing anything from Riccardo di Stefano, Rachel prayed. That would be a cruel trap indeed.

She meant it. In her deepest soul, she was afraid that it was a trap in which she was already snared.

They sat down to dinner even later than usual. Rachel had not managed to find where she was supposed to be sitting but Riccardo took her by the elbow and propelled her into a chair beside his own at Anders' table. From Judy's glare, Rachel inferred that this was not at all what her stepmother had intended.

'Now,' he said.

Waiters brought tureens of some gourmet soup. The smell was delicious but Rachel found she could not eat a mouthful with Riccardo di Stefano watching her. His deep-set eyes had laughter lines at the corners. At the moment he was not laughing.

'What did you say your name was?'

Rachel sat ramrod-stiff. 'Rachel McLaine.'

'McLaine.' He thought about it, then shook his head. 'And not a sports professional to amuse the guests. So what exactly is it that you do for Anders?'

'Nothing at all,' snapped Rachel. She was not so young that she could not spot innuendo. Her loathing of Riccardo di Stefano increased to a new record. 'My step-mother is a house guest.' Thus she neatly disclaimed any association with Anders herself.

He pursed his lips in a soundless whistle, looking across the table at Judy. 'Stepmother, is it?'

Rachel flushed. Even with her intentions towards Anders becoming painfully clear, Judy could not quite keep the hunger out of her eyes when she looked at Riccardo di Stefano.

Rachel said sharply, 'My father thought she needed a break.'

His eyes mocked. 'And you came along for a free ride?'

She hated him so much then. She could think of nothing more satisfying than to confirm all his prejudices.

'And the free beach, the free parties and the free champagne,' she agreed, baring her teeth in a smile that should have turned his blood cold.

It had no noticeable effect. In fact he did not even look surprised. If she had not sensed that deep, controlled anger earlier, Rachel would have said she was boring him. She was so furious that she went on the offensive.

'And what's your reason for being here?'

That did startle him. He did not look pleased but at least this time he looked at her as if he realised there was someone there. It was exhilarating.

'I was on holiday,' he said with bite.

'Was?'

' "A peaceful break" was what they said. No one was supposed to know how to get hold of me.'

Rachel looked round at the party and lowered her lashes as she had seen Judy and Monkey do. She mocked him with an innuendo of her own.

'Oh, boy, did you come to the wrong place if you didn't want to be got hold of.'

Riccardo's eyes narrowed. 'I take it we've met before? I mean before that charming pastoral interlude this afternoon.' His voice was cynical.

That hurt. She was not going to let him see how much. So Rachel widened her eyes at him as innocently as she could manage. 'Well, I've heard a lot of your advance publicity today. Does that count?'

For a moment he looked as if he was about to burst into flames. 'If it meant that you came looking for me, it counts,' he said. He sounded grim.

Rachel quailed. She was not going to let him see that either. 'Why should I come looking for you?'

'The pastoral idyll,' he drawled. 'Rather a good ploy with a man who is known to be looking for—peace.'

Rachel sat very straight in her spindly chair. Suddenly she did not want to play games any more. She spat, 'Just what are you implying?'

'Implying? Nothing. I'm congratulating you on your tactics, Rachel McLaine.'

The drawl was more pronounced and his lids dropped steeply, hiding his expression. But his whole attitude, from the lounging body to the lazy voice, was insolent. Calculatedly insolent, Rachel thought. Only just on this side of downright insult and quite deliberately so.

Rachel would not have believed mere words could hurt her so much. She actually caught her breath at the pain. Then she rallied. She had promised herself she would teach him a lesson. By heaven, he deserved that someone should do just that.

So she said with contrived sweetness, 'I'm flattered, of course. But I don't quite see what there is to congratulate me on.'

'Don't you? Everyone else here does.'

She raised her eyebrows.

'I wouldn't have spent the afternoon with any other woman here,' he explained in a reasonable voice. 'They know it, too.'

Rachel gasped. For a moment her eyes blazed. Riccardo laughed.

'Your marketing strategy is impressive,' he told her softly. 'It's a great skill—not to let the punter know he is being marketed to. You're a natural.'

Rachel went cold with a fury she would not have believed herself capable of. Her feelings towards Anders and Judy paled in comparison with it. She even forgot her betrayed and hoodwinked father in her outrage.

She said chokingly, 'At least I'm not a playboy. A vain, silly playboy.'

He leaned back in his chair, toying with his wineglass. He did not even look annoyed.

'Rude,' he said, sounding pleased. 'A shift of marketing strategy? Or do you get upset when your target sees through you?'

Rachel had got hold of herself. She managed a smile, though her cheeks felt as if they would crack with the effort. 'Only when everyone else is falling over themselves to lay out the red carpet. I like to think of it as redressing the balance.'

'You're quick to make judgements.'

She put her head on one side. 'Oh, I don't think so. I've been watching a pretty nauseating display ever since you arrived this evening.'

Across the table Letitia Lambert drew in a shocked breath and even her easygoing husband said, 'I *say*, hang on there.'

But Riccardo silenced him with an upraised finger.

'Watching me all evening, were you?' he said softly. 'Now why was that?'

To her fury Rachel found a fiery blush rising to her cheeks. She set her teeth and flung back, 'Doesn't one always watch the main attraction at the circus?'

Letitia Lambert exchanged a shocked look with her husband. 'Ask the waiter how they barbecue the lobster,' she said quickly.

'But we've barbecued our own dozens of times.'

'I want to know how they do it here.'

Ronnie raised a hand to summon a hovering waiter. Riccardo ignored it. He had not taken his eyes off Rachel. He seemed unaware of anyone else.

He drawled, 'Main attraction? Are you trying to flatter me?'

Rachel raised her eyebrows. 'Your standards of flattery can't be very high,' she commented.

He stretched suddenly, his hands clasped at the back of his neck, and gave her a long, slow smile. And what he said was utterly unexpected.

'So why don't you show me some of the high-grade stuff?'

Rachel could not have been more shocked if he had thrown his champagne over her. She blinked, silenced.

There was a short pause. She became aware that other people were watching them openly. Riccardo di Stefano gave her a bland smile. She flushed deeply and turned away. She felt as if she had lost a battle somehow. A public battle.

Waiters came and went, bringing food that Rachel barely touched. She kept her back resolutely turned to Riccardo, talking hard to her other neighbour. She took about as much notice of what he had to say as she did of the food.

The meal finished. Anders made a brief speech, welcoming everyone. He did not, Rachel noticed, mention Judy's birthday.

Afterwards the famous band began to play and the guests started strolling from table to table. The blonde Helen made a beeline for them as soon as Anders sat down. She flung her arms round Riccardo's neck from behind.

'Wonderful Ricky,' she said, nuzzling his ear. 'I waved but you weren't looking. Are you losing your touch?'

He turned and flicked her chin. 'It seems like it,' he said drily.

Helen laughed. 'Oh, not with me, lover. Never with me. But, from what I could see, you haven't cracked the thought police.' And she sent a malicious look across at Rachel.

Rachel stiffened. Riccardo looked from her to Helen and back again.

'You've lost me.' He was drawling, the last word in sophisticated unconcern.

Helen gave a tinkling laugh. 'Didn't you know, darling? Rachel—it is Rachel, isn't it?—is here to make sure that Judy doesn't stray *too* far off the straight and narrow. At least, not while anyone important is looking.'

Riccardo raised his brows. His expression was unreadable. Rachel felt as if her feelings would boil over and scald them all. Abruptly she turned her shoulder and began to talk to her other neighbour. She was aware of Riccardo taking Helen off to dance but she did not look round as they went.

The music became louder and more insistent. Voices rose. More and more people began to dance. Rachel's neighbour went too, with an apologetic look as he was swept off into the crowd.

'Looks like you'll have to dance with me, then, my siren.' The husky voice was low, as if only she was meant to hear. As presumably she was.

There was something faintly threatening about it. Rachel froze. She looked round. Those who were not dancing were talking noisily or sipping champagne so cold that it frosted the glasses. For once, nobody seemed to be taking any notice of Riccardo di Stefano. Except her.

She lifted her chin and looked at him. Throughout the evening his manner could have added several inches of ice to those glasses. Now he was looking warm and lazy and—worst of all—as if it was all her doing.

Rachel sat very stiff in her chair. She was certain that she was being mocked—and by a master. She did not

like it. But this was a new ploy and she did not know
how to handle it at all.

Feeling horribly gauche, she said, 'This is not really
my sort of party. I don't think I'll—'

Riccardo twirled one of the spindly chairs round and
sat down astride it. He smiled at her from under his
lashes. Rachel's stomach turned over. She found she was
grasping the arm of her patio chair rather tightly. She
let it go—but not before Riccardo had seen that con-
vulsive grip. His smile widened. 'I was thinking the very
same thing.'

Young and inexperienced she might be, but she was
not an idiot. It was quite clear what he was thinking and
it was as far away from her own ideas about how to
spend the rest of the evening as you could get.

She said levelly, 'I didn't quite finish my book this
afternoon. I really want to know what happens. I'd like
to read for a bit before I go to sleep.'

She thought he would mock. Once again he confounded her with the unexpected. 'You'll miss the
birthday cake.'

'I'm not hungry,' Rachel announced defiantly.

'Aren't you?' He seemed surprised. 'I am.'

He let his eyes smile straight into her own. She could
not pretend not to know what he meant. What was more,
the sexual challenge might be contrived but it never-
theless had a shocking effect on Rachel. Her stomach
turned several back-flips and started to tremble like an
earthquake warning.

Humiliatingly, Riccardo knew it. He had to know it.
His experience would have told him even if he had not
seen the tell-tale tremors of her fingers against the arm
of the chair.

His experience was not sufficient, however, to hide
the small gleam of triumph in his eyes. Rachel saw it.
It fired up all her pride in one glorious surge of anger.

'Stop it,' she choked. 'Just stop it.'

She rose to her feet and bent her eyes on him with a
sulphurous expression. Now they were beginning to at-

tract attention. Rachel was in too much of a temper to notice, however.

'Don't think you can play your silly games with me,' she said, bravely ignoring her scarlet cheeks and trembling limbs. Her tone was utterly contemptuous. 'I'm not one of your fan club. And I don't want to do business with you, either. I don't have to take this. And I won't.'

She stalked off through the tables, horribly conscious of the amused glances that followed her. Riccardo di Stefano was not unconscious of them either. He did not follow her but as she went he watched her. And his expression was no longer amused.

Still shivering with temper—she told herself firmly that it was temper—Rachel skirted the dancers. There was a small group by the pool, not dancing. As Rachel approached she saw the shoulder-borne camcorders and the businesslike cameras. This, then, must be the Press. They looked alarmingly well equipped.

Rachel hesitated. This was the reason why Judy had wanted her at the party. Should she join them? There was no sign of Judy. Anders was sitting on one of the pool loungers, waving a cigar as he held forth. But he was alone apart from his audience.

Rachel was beginning to turn away when one of the photographers saw her. Anders looked up at once. He waved imperatively.

'Damn,' muttered Rachel.

But she went over to him. There was reluctance in every muscle but she went.

'Mrs McLaine's stepdaughter, gentlemen,' he said, urging her into the lounger beside him and putting a heavy arm round her shoulders.

It was all Rachel could do not to shudder. For Daddy, she reminded herself, and pinned on a dazzled smile. For a moment the click of camera shutters almost drowned out the cicadas. And then the questions started.

'Been to the Caribbean before?'

'How does it feel to be among the beautiful people for the first time?'

'What do you want to be, sweetheart? Model? Actress?'

And then, sneering and somehow gleeful, a voice asked, 'How long have you known Rick di Stefano?'

Rachel unfocused her eyes and looked round at them all as if she were too dim to understand what they were implying. I hate this place and I hate these people, she thought. I'm never coming near people like this ever again as long as I live. I don't care what Judy or Daddy or *anyone* says. Never again.

And then help came from an unexpected quarter. Judy appeared on the terrace. The whole tribe turned their cameras on her. She tossed her hair, laughing. Then she was strolling down the steps to the kidney-shaped pool, unbuttoning her gold dress as she came.

When she arrived in front of Anders and Rachel she stopped. She ignored Rachel, her whole concentration bent on Anders. Her head tilted provocatively. Anders lounged there, looking up at her, not moving.

Judy gave a soft laugh. Rachel was shocked. She had never heard any sound so intimate, so wholly adult in her life, she thought. Then, quickly, Judy shrugged off her gold dress. It fell over his legs. He made no attempt to move it.

Rachel and the whole crew of press men held their breath.

Underneath the evening gown, Judy wore a lacy bikini that left very little to the imagination. Nor did the look she sent Anders.

Rachel shrank back in an agony that was part embarrassment, part something far deeper. She felt desperately shaken. Judy had said Rachel did not understand how she felt about Anders. How right she had been. Looking, flinching, Rachel saw that it was as if there were only the two of them in the whole world. As if Judy did not even remember she had a husband, much less care about him.

With a toss of her head that was frankly challenging, Judy kicked off her shoes and dived into the pool. The cameras swirled round, following her. The oil magnate got to his feet, stripped off his jacket, and followed her.

Rachel could not bear it. The cameras trained away from her at last, she leaped to her feet and ran into the arbour. Straight into the arms of the man waiting in the shadows. The impact knocked the breath out of her.

He kissed her. She knew who it was.

At last he lifted his head. 'It may not be your sort of party,' said Riccardo di Stefano unevenly, 'but you seem to be stuck with it.'

Rachel hauled herself away from him as far as he would let her go. His dark hair was stirring in the faint breeze from the sea. For a moment he represented everything she hated at the Villa Azul.

'Don't bet on it,' she snarled.

'Coward,' he said softly.

That brought Rachel's chin up so sharply that the hibiscus flower in her hair jerked dangerously.

'I'm not a coward.'

His mouth twitched. She was positive that he was laughing at her. Anger came another critical centimetre closer to the surface.

He absently tucked the hibiscus back into place. Rachel felt his fingers, warm and deft, just brush her ear, then touch that devastatingly vulnerable spot behind it.

In spite of her anger at him and all he represented, she shivered with longing. Just for a moment, Riccardo looked startled. His arms tightened.

Behind them there was a sudden surge of laughter. Rachel stood like a steel column in Riccardo's arms. She could not even imagine what Judy had said or done to have caused that ribald shout. She felt ashamed—and desperate that he should not see it.

She said in a hard voice, 'Let me go.'

He shook his head. 'Not a chance. You can either come back to the party and dance with me of your own accord, or I carry you.'

Rachel glared. 'Bully-boy tactics.'

'If you like.' He was implacable.

'I thought playboys stuck to charm.'

He smiled then, as if he was really amused. 'Ah, we do. But only as long as it works. Which, in your case, it clearly doesn't.'

'And nor will throwing me over your shoulder like a barbarian raider,' she flashed.

He burst out laughing. Rachel could have hit him. Or burst into tears. Both possibilities were equally awful to contemplate.

'Oh, why couldn't you—?' She broke off, pain tearing at her.

There was no way she could say what she really felt. She felt betrayed—partly by Judy, whose performance tonight had rocked Rachel to her foundations, but worse—far worse—by Riccardo himself.

He had hurt her, Rachel realised, dazed. He had hurt her more than anyone had ever hurt her in her life. And all because he was not what he'd seemed. No, not even that. It was because he was not what she had thought he was. Instead he was, as everyone else knew, one of the Villa Azul's beautiful people: sophisticated and amoral and cold to the bottom of his soul.

You couldn't say to a man like that, Oh, why couldn't you be what I thought you were? Rachel thought. He would only laugh. And serve her right.

She was shaking as she levered herself away from him.

She said as if she hated him, 'I'm not dancing with you. Or anyone else in this beastly place.'

Riccardo's arms slackened. He held her away from him, a look on his face that said he was going to demand an explanation. Rachel knew she could not afford that.

Before he knew what she was about, she had wrenched herself out of his grasp and fled.

She meant to go straight back to her cabin but she was too restless. Instead she walked along the beach, trying to remember her life in England, the school she had left, the college she hoped to go to if her exam results were good enough. But it all seemed unreal somehow. Her mind kept breaking back to the Villa Azul. The problems it posed were insoluble.

Rachel was kicking up the sand, thinking ferocious thoughts about Judy and Anders, when she realised that the person she was feeling most savage about was Riccardo di Stefano.

What is wrong with me? she thought. Anyone would think I had fallen in love.

She stared out to sea. The stars were brilliant but their reflection was broken up by the restless waves. The breakers looked like stranded monsters reaching for the shore, only to die before they reached it. Seeing it, Rachel shivered. Was she, too, reaching out for something she would never quite touch?

This is nonsense, she told herself. You can't fall in love in a day.

But the poets she had read at school said you could fall in love in an hour, in a moment. She had thought it was silly. She had thought it was just an excuse to write their poems. She thought she had even said so in one of her examination essays. Now—

I'm going home, she decided.

She had an open ticket, which she now realised Anders had probably paid for. Judy must have wanted to keep her options open to stay on. Well, the advantage of that was that she could take off whenever she wanted.

Tomorrow morning. When everyone else is still recovering from the party. I'll get Ben to drive me to the airfield. I'll get the first plane to Antigua or Barbados and then any plane I can back to London.

And then you'll never see Riccardo di Stefano again, said an unwelcome voice in her head.

That's just fine.

But you want to.

No, I don't.

This afternoon you thought he was the most exciting man you'd ever met.

Rachel cast another look at the restless sea and its eternal hungry surge for the shore.

'This afternoon he wasn't Riccardo di Stefano,' she said aloud.

This afternoon he had been a challenging stranger. There had been a hint of danger about him, perhaps— a sense that she did not really know him or what he would say or do in any given situation. But she had not known about his millions, his reputation—or his groupies. It was like recognising a truth one had been hiding from.

It was surprising how much it hurt. Rachel's head went back as if the surging sea had struck her.

Oh, she had to leave the Villa Azul all right. If she did not, Riccardo di Stefano was going to find out that she was in love with him.

CHAPTER FIVE

RACHEL rushed back to her cabin, determined to pack. But when she got there she found a dark figure sitting on the low wall in front of it. She stopped dead. It had to be Riccardo. Her heart leaped into her throat. But she knew this was a confrontation she could not avoid.

She went forward bravely.

'What are you doing here?'

Only it was not Riccardo. It was a short, slim man with one of those cameras that looked like a long-range weapon. Which, she supposed, it was, in a way. He stood up.

'Hi, Rachel,' he said cheerily, as if they'd known each other all their lives. 'That was a great shot I got of you.'

Rachel stopped dead. She thought of all she had heard about the paparazzi. And then Judy's performance tonight. Her heart leaped in an entirely different way. She wished passionately that she was older, more experienced. Or at least less alone. Don't antagonise him, she told herself.

So she said pleasantly, 'I'm glad. When do I get to see it?'

He was surprised. Then he laughed, sounding almost admiring. 'Won't make tomorrow's papers in Europe. Too late. Any day after that. Depending...'

He left it up in the air. She thought, He is waiting for me to protest. So she would not protest. Instead she went up to the little house and put on the terrace light.

'I'll look out for it,' she said over her shoulder, quite as if she did not care.

He followed her, peering into her face. 'Has McLaine's gone bust? Judy left your Dad? Did you know that when

79

you came with her? How you finding life at the Villa
Azul?'

She answered the only one that was not a minefield.
'Out of this world,' said Rachel with irony.

He missed the irony. 'Gonna stay?'

She said carefully, 'My stepmother has put a lot of
effort into giving me a good time, but we both know it's
only a holiday.'

He looked at her, his sharp little face disappointed.
'You saying she came to the Villa Azul so you could
party? Pull the other one.'

Rachel smiled. 'Well, if you've done your background research, you must know I've never been anywhere like this before. And without Judy I never would
have come now.'

He chewed his lip. 'Yeah. But...'

She looked at her watch as if she were waiting for
someone. He picked it up at once, as she meant him to.

'Meeting someone?'

'I think I've already met him.'

She remembered how Helen had looked in the mirror.
She attempted the cat-like smile, implying all sorts of
things she could not have put a name to.

It seemed to work. He was impressed in spite of
himself.

'Rick di Stefano?'

He also sounded as if he did not really believe it.

Rachel's shrug was innuendo all on its own. 'I look
forward to the photographs. Enjoy yourself. Goodnight.'

She closed the door firmly behind her.

She thought the photographer might try to follow but
all she heard was a disconsolate, 'Night,' as he trailed
away. She hadn't closed it properly. The door swung back
open again, letting in the sounds of the sea and the cicadas. But the photographer did not return.

Rachel switched on the indoor light. She was trembling. She put a hand to the back of her neck to ease
the tension and kicked off her shoes. Her feet felt gritty
on the floor. She looked down.

At some point she must have brought in sand from the beach. There were sandal-shaped prints across the floor and a little swirl in the bathroom doorway, where she must have shaken out her beach towel. It crunched underfoot unpleasantly. It could not stay like that.

She went to a cupboard and got out the small besom with which the cabin was provided. In spite of her trials of spirit, Rachel grinned suddenly.

'Hearts may break but the housework still has to be done,' she remarked aloud.

'How very true,' said a voice from the doorway.

Rachel dropped the broom and swung round. Her heart was in her mouth. When she half expected him he was not there and when she had all but banished him from her mind he turned up, rendering her speechless.

Riccardo di Stefano raised his eyebrows at her expression. 'Why so shocked?' he said smoothly. 'You knew I was not going to leave it at that.'

He was right. Her reaction when she'd first seen the photographer proved that. All her borrowed sophistication deserted her. 'Yes. No. I mean I wasn't sure—'

He laughed, not unkindly, and strolled into the room. 'Be sure.' He took the broom away from Rachel's suddenly nerveless fingers. 'Housework can wait.' His voice was no longer entirely smooth.

Without her shoes, Rachel felt even more overwhelmed by his height. She stepped back. Riccardo propped the besom against the wall and followed.

She said hurriedly, 'What are you doing here?'

He laughed.

'I told you—'

'You want to go to bed with a good book. I know.' He sounded amused but there was still that undertone that was not amused at all.

He prowled closer. Rachel's heart beat under her breastbone like a desperate bird. She thought, I am his prey. Before, he didn't really care very much, but now that he is concentrating on me he will be merciless. She also thought, alarmed, I am still in love with him.

Her eyes flickered. Riccardo gave a low laugh.

'I shall have to change your mind.'

Rachel curbed her alarm. He was a civilised man, she told herself. He might like winding her up but he had a reputation to maintain. Apart from anything else, he did not need to force himself on a woman who did not want him. Not with that fan club lusting after him back at the party.

So she waited until her heart had stopped its panicky beating. Then she said steadily, 'It would hardly be worth your while.'

'You must let me be the judge of that.' The undertone was less under control now. Was it anger?

Rachel stared. What reason did Riccardo di Stefano have to be angry with her? If it had been the other way round, she would have had plenty of cause. But he had treated her like a fool, patronised and deceived her from the moment he'd seen her.

She tried to keep it level but her voice sounded horribly young when she said, 'Haven't you had enough fun at my expense already?'

There were green glints in his eyes. 'Believe me, I haven't even started. Come here.'

Rachel was shaken. 'What?'

But he did not order her again. Instead he took one long step forward and took her in his arms. He forced her to look up to meet his eyes. It hurt Rachel's neck. He was too tall, too wide-shouldered; he blocked out everything. In spite of all her good sense, Rachel felt her head begin to swim.

'Don't pretend,' Riccardo said roughly. 'You've been playing me on a line ever since you saw me this afternoon, haven't you? Well, now you've got me. Don't you want me, after all, sweetheart?'

Rachel swallowed. 'I don't know what you mean.'

But her voice was shaky. She had promised herself she would make him sorry. How had he found her out? It was stupid. She regretted it bitterly. She did not think Riccardo was going to believe her regrets, though.

'I don't know,' she said again, helplessly.

He held her away from him. 'You know.' His voice was cynical, even weary. 'Would it help if I told you I heard every word you said to that creature with the camera out there?'

The half-truths she had used to fob off the reporter? What relevance did those have to anything? Rachel's eyes widened.

He nodded, as if she had spoken. 'Yes, it did give you away rather.'

She shook her head, bewildered. 'Give me away?'

Riccardo shook her a little—not hard, just as if he was trying to make her concentrate.

'Up to then, I might have been willing to give you the benefit of the doubt.' He sounded mildly regretful. 'But that was a class performance you turned in out there.'

She was so angry that she forgot that Riccardo di Stefano intimidated her. She fought her way out of his arms and backed to the wall, glaring.

'How kind,' she spat. 'Class performance. I'm really flattered.'

He gave a low laugh. But he did not look amused. His eyes were cold and watchful.

'I can see you are. I take it you've finished your experiment for tonight?'

'What?'

'Experiment,' repeated Riccardo di Stefano casually. 'Isn't that what it was? A little flattery, a little stroking. How much can I get away with without having to pay my dues?'

Rachel realised with an unpleasant shock that he was seriously angry. In fact 'angry' was hardly the word for the cold rage beating at her across the little cabin.

She was tired and not entirely proud of herself but she was still not answerable for her actions to Riccardo di Stefano.

So she tossed her head and said, 'What's wrong with experimenting a little?'

'And this is the girl who took me to task for being a playboy,' he mocked. 'There's a name for what you were doing this evening, you know.'

She shrugged. His eyes flickered. She was suddenly aware of her bare shoulders cooling in the evening air. She lifted her chin and stared straight back in defiance.

'So?'

'So I think that makes us equal,' he said softly.

Quite suddenly, Rachel began to feel thoroughly out of her depth. She looked over her shoulder, harried. She had nowhere to retreat to. He saw her dilemma. His smile grew.

'What do you mean, equal?' Rachel wished her voice had not quavered on the last word.

The green glints in his eyes made him look positively satanic. 'I mean you lost the moral high ground tonight. If you ever had it. Which, with hindsight, I doubt.'

Rachel was pressing back against the wall so hard that she could feel her hair catching on the rough plaster. 'I don't know what you're talking about,' she said contemptuously. But there was a distinct tremor in her voice.

Riccardo laughed. He came so close that Rachel could feel the heat of his body. He leaned forward, one hand pressed against the wall behind her head. If she'd turned her head, Rachel could have touched his flexed knuckles with her mouth. She could smell wine and the crisp cotton of his shirt, and some other odour that was entirely masculine, entirely Riccardo. She caught her breath.

'You are *not* intimidating me,' she announced.

'So I should hope. If you can handle the paparazzi you can handle me. A high-grade diplomat like you.'

He put his other hand on the wall by her head, effectively pinning her in place. Rachel's heart beat fast but she refused to let him see how nervous he was making her. She looked scornful.

'Now who's being childish?'

Riccardo showed no sign of remorse. He said thoughtfully, 'There is a child in all of us. Sometimes a good child, sometimes a naughty one. This afternoon, I thought I was letting a good child down lightly.' He paused and surveyed her deliberately. 'But I am re-appraising the situation.'

Rachel said furiously, 'I am not a child.'

Quite suddenly he was not laughing any more. 'Quite.'

'I—'

In the corner, the broom clattered to the floor with a sound like a gun going off. Rachel gave a small scream, out of sheer tension. Riccardo gave her a disparaging look. But he straightened and lounged away from the wall to pick up the broom.

'What an extensive repertoire you have,' he marvelled. He sounded savage all of a sudden. He threw the broom away from him with quite unnecessary force. 'Home-maker. Diplomat. The siren on combat duty. Now, she was very beguiling. But I think my favourite so far has been the trembling innocent. You're good at that.'

He looked her up and down, where she stood pressed against the wall. There was something in his eyes which froze Rachel to the spot. He smiled. It was not a pleasant smile.

'Which one will it be in bed, I wonder?'

Her mouth went dry. Civilisation was out and anger was in but this was unbelievable. He might be angry with her but he still could not make love to her against her will. She said so.

'Who said it would be against your will?'

'I did,' said Rachel with the firmness of desperation.

She stared at him, quivering. Riccardo was unimpressed, dismissing her protest with a shrug. He hooked a finger into his bow-tie and undid it with a single pull. For some reason the little movement was more threatening than anything else that he had said or done yet.

'You don't mean it,' she said breathlessly. 'I'm not a fool. This is a game to you.'

He lobbed the tie away from him.

Rachel said, 'You're not serious.'

The jacket followed the tie. Neither Rachel nor Riccardo broke eye contact to see where the garments fell.

'I'm always serious when I play games.'

Rachel shook her head. She felt dazed. He did not mean it. He could not. She looked at his expression and realised she was wrong. He meant it.

Riccardo di Stefano cancelled the distance between them and reached for her in one smooth movement.

'Oh, Lord,' she said as her feet left the ground. She clung onto him purely for balance.

He held her against his chest, looking down at her for a moment. His eyes were assessing. 'Ah, the innocent,' he remarked. 'Interesting.'

He strode over to the bed and dropped her unceremoniously in the middle. The front of the sarong came undone at the rough treatment. Neither broke eye contact to take any notice of that either.

He sat on the side of the bed. Rachel struggled up onto one elbow. 'I don't know what you think you're doing—' she began indignantly.

His expression silenced her. To her intense astonishment Rachel felt her bones begin to melt.

'Yes, you do,' he said softly. 'You know exactly. We're going to do something about those instincts of yours.'

His fingers drifted up the side of her bare arm. Something inside Rachel contracted with longing. Her eyes screwed tight shut with the intensity of it.

'Some of them are in working order, then,' said that amused voice in her ear.

She felt his lips on the side of her neck, her collarbone, brushing aside the tangled sarong. His touch was insistent. He was gentle but utterly determined. And when he reached her quickening breasts she did not even want him to be gentle any more.

She twisted restlessly, her hand tangling wildly in his hair. He lifted his head. Reluctantly, Rachel opened her eyes. He was looking down at her, his chest rising and falling as if he were running a race. She could not bear it. Her head tossed on the pillow, tumbling her hair into crazy disarray. The hibiscus fell away unnoticed.

Slowly, slowly, he raised his head, searching her face. Her gaze was wild. Riccardo met it. He looked implacable. Her lips parted in silent yearning. His eyes flamed.

She felt his breath on her flesh, the beat of his blood. She felt his naked skin, warm as she had never imagined. She trembled, shaken. She knew his need was as harsh and urgent as her own.

Yet, in spite of that, Riccardo was holding back. Rachel felt it, in disbelief. Her fingers clenched like a vice on his upper arms. A groan burst out of her. There was a precipice that she needed to reach, she *had* to reach.

Riccardo seemed to know. He said her name, almost as if he were in pain. And then, and then...

In the end it was not the knowledgeable, dominating man of the world who drove them both over that compulsive edge. It was Rachel herself.

Afterwards he rolled over on his back and stared at the ceiling. Rachel's heartbeat steadied slowly. She felt bewildered. And lonelier than she had ever done in her life.

She thought she would give anything if Riccardo would only take her hand. But his open eyes were fixed on the ceiling fan. He seemed very far away. She realised, with a flash of perception beyond her years, that to be unable to reach the person you were lying beside was one of the cruellest exiles. She did not think she was going to forget that one again.

And there was something else she realised. Judy had said she did not understand. Well, now she did. If Riccardo wanted her there was nothing—*nothing*—she would not do for him. *If* he wanted her. The silence was like a prison sentence.

Rachel folded her lips together and got off the bed. Riccardo turned his head to watch her. She bent her head, rubbing the back of her neck to ease the tension. He shut his eyes briefly.

'Rachel, I didn't mean—'

But she was not to find out what Riccardo had not meant. Because that was when the door of the cabin banged back on its hinges and Judy stormed in.

Nine years later in London Rachel shut her eyes, remembering. Even over the distance of years, her whole body convulsed in an agony of shame.

Later she'd discovered that Judy had just tried to persuade Anders to marry her if she got a divorce. Anders had laughed. Rejected, Judy had been hurt and spitting mad. She'd gone to Rachel's cabin looking for a fight. She'd found it.

For a moment Judy stood in the doorway, frozen. Then pure venom took over. Rachel blinked and shrank.

At once Riccardo stood up. 'Enough,' he said.

Such was his authority that Judy stopped, in mid-vituperation. He strolled forward, magnificently unconscious of his nakedness. Rachel groped round for the rags of her sarong. She was appalled.

'This,' he said to Judy, 'is none of your business. Out.'

And, to Rachel's amazement, her stepmother turned and went. Riccardo turned back to her.

'I seem to owe you an apology,' he said formally.

He was as remote as the moon. The man who had called out her name in something like agony might never have existed. Rachel shrank even more. She did not know what to say. She could not bear to look at him. She was afraid of what she would see in his face: indifference, embarrassment or, worse, regret. She wished he could not see her either.

But he could, and seemed to have no trouble in reading her reactions. He sighed.

'Don't look like that. It's not the end of the world.'

Rachel found herself wishing passionately that it was. She did not say so. She did not say anything.

He hesitated. 'I take full responsibility but—'

Rachel flinched. She could not help it. He was going to say that they had both been carried away and she was not to make too much of it. She almost hated him for that.

But she was still in love with him and it was total desolation. She put out an instinctive hand to ward off whatever he was going to say.

He said quietly, 'I never meant to hurt you. I didn't think.'

Rachel nodded jerkily, not meeting his eyes. 'I know. Nor did I.'

'Well, then—'

'These things happen all the time,' Rachel said, before he could.

But she had read him wrongly.

'No, they don't.' Riccardo was not remote any more, or unreadable. He was furious. 'Not to me.'

She shrugged. 'Then chalk it up to new experience.' She thought she would die of the pain. But she sounded flippant. In fact she could almost convince herself that she was utterly cool and in control. It was some consolation.

He took an impatient step forward, then curbed himself.

'You're beat,' he said curtly. 'We'll talk in the morning.'

But in the morning she was on her way to the airport in Anders' limousine, with her stepmother as escort.

In contrast with her venom of last night, Judy was oddly triumphant.

'You always were a slyboots. A cold, self-righteous, *stupid* slyboots.'

Rachel had not slept. After Riccardo had left she had packed. Then she'd gathered the sarong around her like a shawl and sat in the window, waiting for dawn. She was now too tired to reply to Judy's taunts.

'Sneering at Anders and the rest of us like that. Going off with your books and pretending to be so holy. The crazy thing is, you convinced me. You convinced everyone. We thought you didn't even know what you were passing up.'

Rachel leaned her head back against the cushioned headrest and tried to ignore the shrill voice.

'You won't be so smug now, will you? You're down here with the rest of us now.'

Rachel said wearily, 'I can't argue with that.'

Judy laughed. 'And of all the men in the world! The moment Riccardo di Stefano walked in.'

'No,' said Rachel loudly.

Judy laughed again. 'Oh, yes. We all saw it. You're an open book, you stupid child.'

Rachel kept her eyes very wide and refused to cry. Her ordeal was nearly over. The limousine was pulling up outside the shack that was the small island's airport.

Judy gave vent to one final flurry of malice. 'We'll see what your father says about his idolised little girl *now.*'

Nine years later Rachel remembered exactly what her father had had to say and shuddered. He'd met her at the airport and delivered it in one comprehensive speech. After that, he'd driven her to a friend's house and never seen her again.

For weeks Rachel was numb. Even Judy, when she returned to London, was taken aback. She arranged to meet Rachel and gave her some money to tide her over.

In fact, Rachel thought afterwards, it was, perhaps, just as well that the practical problems were so enormous. In facing them, she began also to face her own feelings. There was no question of going to university without her father's financial support. So she had to find a job. Although she did not admit it to herself, she was half waiting for Riccardo di Stefano to arrive in London and save her from her predicament. He never did.

In the end she found Brian Gray and his family. She began to go to night school. She passed crucial examinations. Eventually she stopped waiting for Riccardo.

Eventually the only thing she wanted was never to see him again. She began to think she would manage that.

Until today. Rachel rubbed her hands over her tired eyes. It was all back, as clearly as if she had only just got off that plane. She bit back a cry of shame. For, whatever she'd thought, then or later, about Riccardo di Stefano's seduction, there was one thing she could not disguise from herself. He was older, more experienced and infinitely more cynical than she, but in one thing they had been equals: she had wanted him quite as much as he'd wanted her.

The fact had been so difficult to live with that she had wiped it out of her memory. Or she had thought she had, until today. That must be why she had been so hard on Alexandra, she realised suddenly. Riccardo di Stefano was not forgotten and poor Alexandra had been picking up the punishment for a younger Rachel's mistakes.

She bit her lip, remorseful. What had happened at the Villa Azul was *history*. It had nothing to do with Alexandra, or with the person Rachel herself was these days. She straightened her shoulders. Anything she might have to say in the future to Riccardo di Stefano was going to be professional and nothing but professional, she vowed.

But that small room, the tangled sheet, the wide shoulders, slick and warm under her hands...

'Forget it,' she said to herself, clenching her fists in concentration. 'Forget it, forget it, *forget* it.'

She banished it. There was a job to be done. She was the one to do it and she knew it. She could not allow herself to be deflected. Rachel had to meet her team for discussion and then it was back into the boardroom.

At first she thought no one was there. That did not surprise her, or worry her. Normally she liked to be early, to set up her presentation. On this occasion she'd thought she would probably have to do it all under the impatient eyes of her intended audience. So it was with a sigh of relief that she registered the empty chairs. Clearly the board lunch was running on.

She began to set up the slide projector and checked that her notes and the slides were in corresponding order. Her notes were on small cards which she could hold in one hand. It was an orderly task and she relished it. She was even humming to herself before an unexpected voice spoke.

'I see you like to be prepared.'

Rachel jumped. She stopped humming. After those vivid memories, the sound of that voice made her feel a little sick. She turned round very carefully.

Riccardo di Stefano raised his eyebrows. He strolled forward.

'I seem to have shocked you. Sorry.'

He did not sound the least bit sorry, Rachel thought. Nor did he look sorry. But he did look curious. Her shock must be showing.

That was dangerous. She pulled herself together.

She said with as much calm as she could command, 'I didn't realise anyone was here.'

His eyebrows rose higher. They were strongly marked. Why hadn't she remembered that? He was not a friendly pirate any more. Today he was looking satanic. Those eyebrows gave him the air of a devil, and what was more, a devil with a special line in mockery.

Had he always been like that? She remembered cynicism and anger and, in the end, a passion that had seared her to the soul. She did not remember mockery.

Stop that, she told herself, shaken. Long forgotten, right?

Of course, he was older, and even more successful these days. He would not be the same person she remembered, any more than she was after all these years. She became conscious that he was watching her narrowly.

The mockery intensified. 'Do I disturb you?'

'Of course not,' Rachel said sharply.

She bent her head and riffled blindly through the memo cards she had just put into order. She could feel him watching that too.

He said in a thoughtful tone, 'You know, I have the oddest feeling about you, Mrs Gray.'

Rachel's mouth went dry. 'Oh?' she said, trying to sound indifferent.

'Yes. Increasing by the minute.'

Rachel concentrated on her task. She knew he wanted her to ask what sort of feeling. She was not going to give him that satisfaction, she promised herself. So she shrugged, not looking up.

'Really?'

'Don't you look at people who are talking to you?' he demanded. There was a distinct edge to his voice.

It was a challenge she could hardly avoid. It made her furious but there was nothing she could do about it. Rachel gave an elaborate sigh and straightened.

She still did not quite dare to meet his eyes. But by dint of looking just to the left of his ear she gave a very fair impression of looking at him directly. Riccardo di Stefano's expression was frankly speculative.

'You're quite sure we haven't met before?'

She did not know what to say. There was a pause. His mouth tilted.

'Because, you know, I have the strangest feeling that we know each other. Very well indeed.'

CHAPTER SIX

RACHEL'S fingers tightened involuntarily. Her hands were sweating. She could feel the stiff little cards getting slippery.

'I told you, I was away—'

'The last time I came by,' he finished. 'Yeah, yeah. But the world is not bounded by Bentley's boardroom. Maybe we bumped into each other some other place? Another time?'

The cards shot out of her hands, fanning out across the carpet in total confusion. Rachel gave an exclamation of dismay and fell to her knees, gathering up the cards clumsily. She had difficulty in getting hold of them. Her hands were shaking.

'Allow me.'

Riccardo di Stefano bent and gathered the cards in one hand, like a gambler. He straightened. Rachel had to get up as well, perforce. He was a lot closer now. He put the cards on the lectern and considered her thoughtfully.

'Thank you,' she said. Her throat hurt.

He ignored that. He was smiling and his eyes were bright green. 'You know, I've heard a lot about you, Mrs Gray. A lot of good things from a lot of people. None of them said you were as jumpy as a cat on a hot spot.'

Rachel was tempted to ask the identity of his informants. For a moment she almost did. Then it occurred to her that it would only prolong the conversation.

She said carefully, 'I think your bombshell this morning was enough to make anybody jumpy.'

He looked amused. 'Yes, that they did mention.'

'Mention?' Rachel was confused. 'What?'

'You think on your feet.'

She could feel the guilty colour in her cheeks.

'Now are you going to tell me why I scare the hell out of you? Or are you going to let me have fun working it out?'

There was no answer to that. Rachel looked down, picking up the cards pointedly. She could feel him looking at the top of her head, feel his annoyance. He was balked and he knew it.

Let him stay balked, she prayed.

He gave a quick, annoyed laugh. 'OK, I get the message. You want to get your presentation in order.'

'That was why I came to the boardroom early.'

'And there was me thinking you were stalking me,' he said silkily.

For a moment she did not realise it was a joke. Her eyes flew up to his in pure horror. She had no time to disguise her reaction. His brows twitched together in surprise. His lips parted as if he was going to demand an immediate explanation.

Rachel leaped in to forestall him.

'Please—I haven't got much time.' She gestured at the lectern, the slide projector.

There was a frozen second when she thought he was going to insist on his explanation there and then, no matter what her excuse. Rachel's head went back and, behind her back, she crossed her fingers in a gesture that was pure childhood superstition.

Then at last di Stefano drew back. Reluctantly, it seemed.

'And I've interrupted you.' His voice was heavy with irony. 'Sure. You've made your point, Mrs Gray. But we still have to get together and sort out where we've met before.'

Rachel suppressed her shiver at that. Instead, she gave him one of her best unfocused smiles and said, 'I look forward to it.'

For a moment his frustration was undisguised. Then he shrugged. 'See you later, then.'

He sauntered out. Rachel collapsed in the nearest chair.

She could not stay there, of course. She had work to do. And work, as she had good cause to remember, was a great therapy. Thank God for work, she thought.

By the time the meeting reconvened, she was in reasonably good shape. Her work was in order again, her speech ready. Philip ushered the men into their seats. Rachel took a deep breath, avoided looking at Riccardo di Stefano, and began.

She had learned that the secret of selling her ideas to the board was to keep her presentations short and let them ask questions. That way they got to think they had thought of some of the ideas themselves. That made them better disposed to accept them. No one had ever noticed this technique before.

But from the amused way Rick di Stefano watched her throughout her brief introduction Rachel was almost certain that he had detected her strategy. He had found her out and, from the way he toasted her silently with his water glass, was amused by it. Maybe even impressed.

For a moment Rachel almost faltered. Rick di Stefano's amusement increased. Hurriedly she pulled herself together and went on.

The questions came on as she'd expected, in roughly the order she'd expected. She took them all, dealing with them as she had planned. Then came the key one.

'But I can't see how we can pay for it. How will we fund this?'

Tread carefully, Rachel; here come the eggshells, she thought. She avoided Riccardo di Stefano's eye even harder.

'A good question, Mr Barron,' she said to the questioner. 'My proposal is that we take funds away from the Eastern European section and put that on a care and maintenance basis. You will see—' she flipped up a chart on the projector '—we have been losing money in that area for some years. I know we all think it is an investment in the future but, with the position as it is, we

have to look at nearer horizons. At least for the moment.'
She looked around. 'But I'm open to any alternative
suggestions.'

Rick di Stefano said lazily, 'What about if you just
got more money?'

Rachel folded her lips together. 'Since the purpose of
this meeting is to find how to avoid a takeover, I don't
see that as a serious question, Mr di Stefano.'

It was the first time her diplomacy had deserted her
in a gruelling couple of hours. Philip looked at her,
horrified.

He stood up, saying, 'I'm sure it was a serious question
if Mr di Stefano asked it, Rachel. Perhaps—'

Rachel was so angry that she looked directly at Rick
di Stefano for the first time. 'We've borrowed as much
as we can support. If we go for any more we'll have to
pay higher interest or pledge assets—either way, our ex-
isting lenders will get worried. As I explained. If you've
got any options to suggest—apart from selling out, that
is—I'd be happy to hear them.'

Rick di Stefano took no notice of Philip either. He
gave a low laugh. He seemed to be enjoying himself
hugely. 'Some well-wisher might lend you the money.'

'Without additional security? Or taking shares?'
Rachel was scornful. 'You're crazy.'

'Rachel!' Philip sounded almost frantic. 'Rick, look,
maybe we should take a break and think about this.'

'Oh, Mrs Gray has plenty of thoughts, Phil.' He
sounded unoffended, even intrigued. 'Do you want a
breather, Mrs Gray?'

'No,' snarled Rachel.

'I thought not,' he murmured. 'Now let us suppose
that I, for example, might be willing to lend you the
money to fund the change of direction you're talking
about here. What would you say?'

'What?' Philip sank limply back in his chair. He
looked stunned. He was not the only one, including
di Stefano's own team.

Only Rachel and di Stefano stayed cool. Rachel was wary, while di Stefano was relaxed and maddeningly uninvolved.

'Well?' he prompted.

Since it was clear that Philip and the others were in no state to answer him, Rachel said, 'Why?'

He laughed aloud at that. 'Mrs Gray, you are a delight.'

That brought Rachel's chin up. 'If you are asking me to hypothesise something inherently ridiculous,' she said in her most prissy voice, 'you have to give me a reason why I should waste my time.'

'So I see.' The irony was back. Along with something else. Rachel did not know what it was but she was sure it did not bode well for her. 'Well, let us say that I like Bentley's management style more than I expected. Will that do?'

Seeing the no which was forming on Rachel's lips, Philip rushed into speech.

'Of course, of course,' he said heartily. 'You can do a simulation on the basis of borrowed funds, can't you, Rachel? Do you want to go and put it in the computer?'

'I don't need a computer,' Rachel said evenly.

She looked down at her painfully composed slides and picked up a marker. 'You assume increased inflow of another—what shall I say, Mr di Stefano? One million?'

'One million seems reasonable,' he agreed gravely.

The board gave a collective gasp. You could feel the level of hope rising, Rachel thought. Why could they not see what he was doing? She put a slash through both totals so heavily that she broke the point of her marker.

She went on, 'On the balance sheet you increase borrowing. On the outflow side you use it by retaining the East European desk, maybe add a little lending.' She picked up a fresh marker and adjusted those totals too. 'So the assets go up a little. The liabilities go up a lot. And none of the new business will bring in any profit in this year.' She looked round. 'And may I remind you, gentlemen, it is this year which is critical?'

She must look like a small animal at bay in front of her projector, Rachel thought. A small animal, helpless to turn the herd from its self-destructive course. The board had scented reprieve when, only this morning, it had been expecting extinction. They were not going to question Riccardo di Stefano's motives in offering them this last-minute rescue. And nothing Rachel could say would make them ask themselves what was in it for him.

Oh, he was clever. Presumably this was how he'd made his millions in the first place. Walk in, terrify the board and management, then offer them a little hope; then, later, however many months later it took, gobble them up. Why on earth was she the only one to see it?

Across the room, her furious eyes met his. It was a mistake. It was a mistake of incalculable proportions. His eyes were as green as glass. He smiled.

Her heart lurched up into her throat and then down to the centre of the earth. She thought, He *knows*. She stopped arguing.

Rachel escaped to her office while the rest of the board was still gathering round Riccardo di Stefano, telling him what a wise investment he had just made. If only they knew exactly how wise, Rachel thought cynically. But the bank was the last thing on her mind after that shocking moment of eye contact. Her mouth was dry and her head was pounding like a smith's hammer.

'Hi,' said Mandy, looking up. 'Did they buy your reconstruction?'

'At a price,' said Rachel grimly.

She picked up a bottle of mineral water from Mandy's desk, hauled off the top and drank a long draught straight from the bottle.

Mandy stared. She had never seen Rachel do anything like that before. Also, there were droplets of water on the second-best jacket lapel. That could only mean one thing: Rachel's hands were shaking.

'High price?'

Rachel lowered the bottle and wiped a hand across her mouth. 'The highest.'

'For you or the bank?' said Mandy prosaically. She did not believe in identifying with her employers.

Rachel gave a little laugh which broke in the middle. 'I wish I knew.'

She shot into her room and closed her door, only to open it a moment later.

'If anyone calls, I've gone. If anyone turns up here, I've gone.'

Quite bemused, Mandy nodded.

She was not bemused for long. A tall and gorgeous predator strolled into her office and paused at her desk. 'Mrs Gray's office? Don't tell me. She's just gone into conference.'

'Er—no,' said Mandy, thinking that corporate raiders should not be allowed to have warm, green-flecked eyes that made your spine turn to treacle. Manfully, she recalled her instructions. 'I think she's gone for the day.'

Riccardo di Stefano gave a crack of laughter. 'She'll regret that,' he said with confidence, and made his leisurely way through Rachel's door before Mandy could stop him.

Rachel was divesting herself of the checked jacket when the door opened. She did not immediately look round. Not, that was, until a voice said in accents of unholy glee, 'Gone for the day? Not worthy of you, Rachel. Really not worthy. You must have known I'd check.'

Rachel spun round from the cupboard, her expression unguarded. Riccardo was leaning back against the door as if he were some waterfront bum propping up the nearest wall for lack of anything better to do. A waterfront bum with a nasty streak, she corrected herself mentally. One who was not going to move out of the way except in his own good time.

'Check?' she said mechanically. 'Why should you?'

'Secret of my success. Never take anything on trust. Particularly where women are concerned.'

Rachel stood stock-still. She was fighting to stay in control. No matter what she thought she had seen in his eyes back there, there was no proof yet that he remembered anything. Work on the assumption that he is still fishing, she told herself. 'I'm sure it's an excellent strategy.'

'It works for me,' he said lightly. But his eyes were not light.

In her shock at his entrance she had half pulled the front of her blouse out of her skirt. Now her hands began to twist unconsciously in the loose stuff. He took in the signs of agitation. The silence lengthened.

'Well, Rachel,' he said at last, 'it's been a long time.'

Rachel felt as if the floor had dropped out of her well-built office. She adopted her most wooden expression. 'I'm afraid I'm not with you.'

'Same old Rachel,' he said tolerantly. 'Beautiful manners and a stone wall behind them. Still we both know the stone wall comes down in the end, don't we?'

She did not answer. She could not.

He added in a thoughtful voice, 'I should have known you'd go far. I don't know why I never thought of looking for you in the financial world. It was obvious that was where you'd end up, with your father to back you.'

Rachel just stopped herself wincing.

'You know, that was a really good pitch you ran just now.'

'Thank you,' she said in a stifled voice.

His smile grew. 'Never let the punter know he's being marketed to,' he reminded her softly.

So he did remember. Suddenly there was no longer any way she could pretend that she did not understand him. Rachel felt herself whiten.

He was impatient suddenly. 'You look as if you're about to face a firing-squad. Sit down, for God's sake.'

She did.

'That's better.' He strolled forward and propped himself on the corner of her desk, looking down at her with undisguised speculation. 'Little Rachel McLaine. Well, well, who would have thought it?'

Rachel was not playing the social reminiscence game with him. 'Thought what?'

For a moment he looked disconcerted. Then he gave a soft laugh. 'Stop glaring at me. This isn't the Villa Azul. Or do you want to call me a playboy again?'

She was cold with shock inside. But that had been nine years ago and these days Rachel's armour was better. She leaned back in her big swivel chair and crossed one slim leg over the other. 'Does that still rankle?'

Riccardo's eyes still had green flecks in them. Rachel could see them because he was much too close. They still crinkled at the corners when he was amused, too.

'Every day,' he told her solemnly.

Rachel did not want to amuse him. She looked away, biting her lip. 'I'm sorry. That was a fatuous thing to say.'

He smiled. 'Not at all. Nobody likes to be called a playboy. Especially as it was what my father was saying regularly at the time. It rankled all right.'

'Then I apologise.'

'Why should you? As far as you know, it was true.'

'Not from what I read in the papers,' Rachel admitted ruefully.

He leaned even closer. 'You've been reading my press?' His tone sounded dangerously personal.

Rachel drew back a little. 'We keep a cuttings file on important people. Directors, shareholders, main customers—that sort of thing. The big cheeses in general.'

Riccardo was not best pleased. He pulled a face. 'I don't think I've been called a big cheese before.'

'Not to your face, maybe.'

Faint annoyance crossed his face. 'You don't change, do you, Rachel? Still saying it to their faces.'

'Tell the truth and shame the devil,' she said flippantly.

'Meaning me?'

After what she had been thinking about him earlier, she almost jumped. There was a shocked pause. Then she shrugged. 'If the cap fits...'

His eyes narrowed. 'So I'm still cast as the devil, am I, even after all these years?'

This time Rachel was not quite quick enough to censor her own reaction.

There was no point in trying to disguise her hostility. She said coldly, 'Well, you were hardly my guardian angel, were you? What do you expect?'

For a moment he did not speak. When he did, it was on a note of discovery. 'You blame me.'

She had given herself away. She made a desperate attempt to retrieve her mistake. 'It was so long ago—'

'You blame me.'

She moved restlessly in her chair. 'That's a very dramatic way of putting it. I prefer to say I don't feel much affinity with you.'

That amused him. 'Then things have changed indeed. As I recall it, affinity was the one thing we really had. By the truck-load.'

I will not blush, Rachel thought. She was furious. I *will not*.

She said curtly, 'Then our memories differ.'

'Do you think so?'

He considered her. From another man, in another place, with a different history between them, that look would have been almost caressing. From Riccardo, it was sheer, unmitigated provocation. Rachel felt the hair on the back of her neck rise.

'It seems so.'

He shifted. At once she tensed. She could not help it. Riccardo saw it, of course. She saw him take note, thoughtfully, and then store it away for future use.

'Then we should discuss it, don't you think? Have dinner with me.'

'*No.*' It was pure instinct. It did not even pretend to ordinary social courtesy.

His reaction was unexpected. Oh, she remembered that too. He had never been predictable, had he? He should have been offended by her instantaneous rejection. Instead he looked even more thoughtful. If anything it seemed to please him.

He stood up and turned. He was not touching her—the desk between them would have been too wide, even if he had tried—and he showed no sign of attempting it. But Rachel scooted her chair back as far as it would go. Inside she was trembling as she had not trembled for nine years.

'You misunderstand. It was not an invitation.' His voice was pleasant. He even smiled.

Rachel was incredulous. 'You're ordering me to have dinner with you?'

'Oh, I don't think we need go that far, do you? You're a clever lady. You can read the subtext.'

She was so outraged that for a moment she forgot her inner tremors. She stood up and looked him straight in the eye. 'And the subtext is that my job depends on seeing you socially?'

He threw back his head and laughed. His throat was long and tanned. She remembered that too. Out of sight, Rachel's hands clenched into white-knuckled fists.

'I don't think it will be very social, do you?'

She said stonily, 'You haven't answered my question. Do I lose my job if I turn you down?'

'Of course not. That's illegal, isn't it? Even in this backward country.' His eyes started to dance. 'Have you got your office bugged, by any chance?'

She said nastily, 'Up to now I've never thought of it.'

He pursed his lips in a silent whistle. 'Biting. Very biting. You really don't think much of me at all, do you, Rachel McLaine?'

'Gray. My name is Rachel Gray these days.'

'Of course it is.' That did not seem to amuse him quite so much. 'I can't wait to meet Mr Gray.'

'My husband is dead,' Rachel told him quietly.

Riccardo's eyes were hard. 'Then it will just be you and me at dinner.'

'I said no.'

'And I said it's part of your professional responsibilities.'

Their eyes clashed. Rachel drew a long shaky breath.

'Get out of my room.' Her voice was so quiet that it was almost a whisper. 'Unless you want to find yourself on the wrong end of a sexual harassment charge, don't come back.'

They stared at each other in silence for a long moment. Rachel's challenge seemed to hang in the air, like an echo. She was shaking visibly now. She was beyond caring. Riccardo's expression was unreadable.

She said, 'I'm not eighteen years old and friendless any more. This time I'm fighting back.'

Riccardo stiffened. For a moment he seemed to have turned to stone. If she had not known that he was invulnerable on all fronts, she would have said she had landed a body-blow.

He did not say anything but his eyes narrowed to slits of ice. Rachel stood her ground proudly. Then he made an odd abrupt sound, half-laugh, half-protest. And, while she still stood there braced for a blasting from a man who was famous for it, he turned on his heel and walked out.

The light was on in the kitchen when Rachel got home. She went in. Hugh was sitting in the same place she had left him this morning. This time he was munching his way through a sandwich the size of a doorstop. Rachel put down her briefcase and cast her eyes to heaven.

'Heavy day,' he said with a grin. 'Couldn't wait for supper. Even if there is any.'

Rachel jumped guiltily. 'What's in the fridge?'

'One old lettuce and three eggs,' Hugh reported without having to look. He waved the sandwich. 'This is the last of the cheese.'

Rachel laughed but she was remorseful. 'I'm a rotten provider.'

'You could always provide take-away pizza,' he suggested. Hugh adored pizza.

'What about Lexy's diet?'

'She says she's not eating with you any more,' Hugh reported. 'She went to her room. She can have the lettuce,' he added generously.

Rachel sighed. 'Battle still on?'

'Not over till the fat lady sings,' Hugh said peacefully. 'Or until you let her go to whatever it is with Theo Judd.' His interest in his sister's love affairs was remote at best.

Rachel bit her lip. 'It's an all-night party. Tell me honestly, Hugh—do you think I'm wrong?'

Hugh took another mouthful of sandwich. His head shake was not an endorsement of her view. It was a refusal to get involved, and they both knew it.

'You're a great help,' Rachel informed him.

He was unrepentant. 'I'm not my sister's keeper, thank God. Send her back to the wild. That's what she wants.'

Rachel gave a little choke of laughter at this reference to his mother's free-wheeling ménage in southern California. 'But is it what your mother wants? I got the impression she was very busy. And what about Lexy's schooling?'

But Hugh was not to be drawn. He had expressed an opinion, which contradicted all his principles of non-alignment, and he was not to be drawn further.

'I wish I knew what to do,' said Rachel, more to herself than to him.

He finished his doorstop. 'Bin her,' he advised, getting up and going. In the doorway a thought struck him. He looked back. 'Better still, get yourself a man. We need someone to lay down the law round here.'

He watched her stiffen. Before she could say anything he gave her a wide, wicked grin. Then he raised a hand and clattered off upstairs.

'Male chauvinist pig,' Rachel shouted after him.

'Super Shark,' he yelled back cheerfully.

His door slammed. Rachel hoped he was getting on with his homework. She went back to review her store cupboard ruefully. She had spent the weekend working on her reconstruction plan. The need to eat had simply slipped her mind.

The phone rang. It was the mother of Alexandra's best friend, calling to form a parental alliance in the face of a new offensive on the all-night-party front. She had also been Rachel's mentor in the last two difficult years since Brian had died.

'Oh, hello, Gilly. Gosh, do I need some solidarity,' responded Rachel with feeling. 'Lexy's not speaking to me and there's no food in the house.'

'I'll be over in ten minutes,' said her friend.

She was as good as her word, bringing the remains of a substantial stew and a supermarket bag of staples.

'Burning the candle at both ends,' she diagnosed, stocking the refrigerator and making coffee as Rachel stuffed half a week's dirty laundry into the washing machine. 'What you need is staff. Alternatively get the monsters to do their own washing.'

Rachel poured washing powder into a dispenser. 'Hugh would. Though I'm not sure about the quality control. Lexy wouldn't on principle.' She slammed the door shut and programmed the machine. 'Come on. Let's go and take our coffee where we can't hear the machinery of conscience.'

They went into her study. Rachel took a pile of computer reports off the single comfortable seat and plumped up the cushions.

'I like this room,' said Gilly, settling down. 'Books and a desk and a view of the garden. What more could a woman want?'

Rachel perched on the ancient leather chair by her desk.

'A reasonably stocked fridge,' she said drily.

'Yes, what happened there? You're usually so efficient, I hate you.'

Rachel sighed. 'Too busy. Lexy would have reminded me normally, but she's not speaking to me. Essential war despatches only, at the moment.'

Gilly nodded. 'All-night party? Susanna's the same.'

'Susanna doesn't want to go with Theo Judd.'

Gilly shuddered. 'No, thank God. He's a really nasty piece of work. Susanna thinks he carries a knife.'

Rachel bit her lip. 'So do I. I've seen it. But Lexy doesn't believe me. Or she thinks it's glamorous.'

'What on earth does she think she's doing?'

Rachel pushed back her hair with a weary hand. She had not managed to put it up again all through the day. 'You tell me. Looking for a father-figure, maybe.'

'Theo? A *father*-figure?'

'Well, he's so much older—'

'Alexandra's father didn't have designer stubble and a leather jacket with too many pockets,' Gilly interrupted briskly. 'Or no visible means of support—apart from running these terrible raves, of course. Peter thinks he's a drug dealer.'

Rachel gave her a disturbed look but did not say anything.

'Why else would a man his age want to hang around with a bunch of fifteen-year-olds?' said Gilly unanswerably.

Rachel put her hand over her eyes. 'That's what I've been asking myself. But when I say it to Lexy—'

'She thinks she's old enough to choose her own friends.' Gilly nodded.

'And points out the age difference between Brian and me.'

Gilly whistled. 'Shrewd move.'

'No one said she wasn't bright,' said Rachel bitterly. 'She doesn't work. Her exam results are appalling. But she's bright enough, if she'd only choose to do something about it.'

'And you're elected chief torturer to make her do just that?'

'That's about the size of it,' Rachel agreed.

Gilly shook her head. 'Don't even try. You're on a hiding to nothing.'

Rachel leaned back and closed her eyes briefly. 'Hugh says the house needs a man to introduce some discipline.'

Gilly stared. 'Are you pulling my leg?'

Rachel opened her eyes and shook her head.

'My stars.' Gilly looked at her friend cautiously. 'Is there—er—anyone that Hugh has in mind?'

For no reason at all, Rachel thought of Riccardo di Stefano. She looked quickly down at her coffee. 'No.'

'Oh.' Gilly sipped coffee and debated. 'It's a long time since Brian died. You're very young to lock yourself into contract stepmotherhood.'

Rachel shook her head again. This was a conversation they had had before.

'No time,' she said briefly.

Gilly was sad. 'Oh, Rachel. Still?'

Rachel looked away, feeling a fraud. All their friends thought her marriage to Brian Gray had been a highly romantic union between a middle-aged man and his friendless young au pair. When he'd died, they'd tiptoed around her grief as if the last great love affair had come to an end.

She had never been able to tell any of them that it had not been like that. It had been a marriage of convenience from first to last. Brian had been her greatest friend. She had liked him and trusted him and gone to him for advice when she had felt she could trust no one else in the world. But neither of them had ever been remotely in love.

And when she'd married him he'd already known he was dying.

Rachel had found him alone in the kitchen one night after the children had gone to bed. He'd looked at his wits' end. That was when he'd told her.

'I've been talking to Angela. She doesn't seem to be able to take it in. She's very busy with her new life, of course. Which doesn't include the kids. She keeps saying something will turn up.' He banged his fist on the counter-top. 'But it won't. All I've got is maybe a year to find a solution.'

He had had two years in the end. And the solution had been Rachel.

She had never regretted it. She knew that it had not been a one-sided relationship. Brian had given her support in her education and, eventually, her career. He had helped restore her shattered confidence. And he had provided the best reason in the world for her lack of relationships with men.

Now that reason was gone. So either she had to find another one or face up to experiences she had been running away from for nine years.

She said with an effort, 'I'm a contract career lady too.'

Gilly took the hint. 'Alexandra was saying. Long hours?'

Rachel sighed. 'I thought it was going to be just for this single project. You know—a few weeks doing eighteen-hour days and then back to normal. Only, it isn't working out quite like that.'

'It never does,' said Gilly wryly. 'Whenever Peter does any of these one-off assignments, he always ends up with more work at the end of it.' Her husband was an executive in a multinational company.

'Well, unless I'm very careful, it looks as if that's exactly what's going to happen to me,' Rachel said gloomily.

Gilly was scornful. 'Careful? Huh! What can you do about it? If they've realised you can work round the clock, they'll jolly well make sure you carry on doing it.'

Rachel knew that, on the basis of her experience as the wife of a seriously successful senior manager, Gilly knew what she was talking about. On the other hand, Rachel had been gaining some experience of her own since she'd started at Bentley's. She allowed herself a small private smile.

'Well, maybe not.' Rachel swirled her coffee round in its mug. 'There are a couple of male egos that might be brought round to seeing things my way. If I approach them in the right way.'

Gilly looked at her with awe. 'You know the right way?'

Rachel looked up. Her eyes danced suddenly. 'I have a working hypothesis. I'll let you know if it works.'

'If it works, patent it,' Gilly advised, getting up. She kissed Rachel briefly on the cheek. 'Don't bother about the casserole. Alexandra can bring it back any time.' She went.

Rachel went to her room and climbed out of her city suit. She hung it up in her understocked wardrobe and put on jeans and a roomy sweatshirt.

There was no sound from Hugh's room, which meant he was wearing his earphones. Rachel gave silent thanks. She knocked quietly at Alexandra's door but was not really surprised when there was no answer. Alexandra was making a point of her right to privacy at the moment.

Rachel went back to the kitchen and geared herself up for phase two of the working day. She checked the washing machine, put Gilly's stew in the oven and started peeling potatoes. Normally she hated peeling potatoes but today she attacked them with a will, as if they were personal enemies. As the peel fell away, she felt an almost bloodthirsty satisfaction.

'Take that,' she said, gouging a particularly stubborn eye out of one of the larger potatoes.

'Talking to yourself now?' said a voice from the doorway.

Rachel looked up. Her stepdaughter had finally emerged from her room and was draped gracefully against the doorjamb. She was wearing a skintight tube-dress that showed an enticing acreage of pale-skinned bosom and ended halfway down her upper thighs. She was presumably going out.

Rachel bit back her immediate reaction and gave Alexandra a pleasant smile. Dealing with corporate raiders all day gave you some grasp of tactics at least.

'Hi. Hungry?'

'I *was*,' returned Alexandra, no mean tactician herself. 'But when you were so late I thought you weren't coming back this evening. So I've made other arrangements.'

Silently Rachel cursed Riccardo di Stefano. If he had not kept her at bay in her office after that meeting, she would have finished her day's work at a reasonable time and been home when she'd said she would be. Not that that would have prevented Alexandra from making a bid to go out with Theo. But at least it would have meant she did not have an excuse handed to her on a plate.

Rachel skewered another eye out of the potato with quite unnecessary viciousness.

Not looking at Alexandra, she said, 'Where's he taking you? And when is he picking you up?'

A faint frown crossed her stepdaughter's face. In matters of detail Theo was proving difficult to pin down. Rachel had discovered this by accident and was using her awareness of it sparingly.

Now Alexandra shrugged elaborately. 'No special time. I said, Let's just hang out.'

'Ah,' said Rachel.

She quartered the potato, dropped the pieces in the salted water with the rest and put the pan on to boil. She rinsed her hands and dried them. 'Pity,' she remarked to the wall. 'Gilly's stew smells good.'

'Gilly *likes* cooking,' Alexandra pointed out. She managed to make this indisputable truth into a rebuke.

'She's also got a cordon bleu qualification,' said Rachel, stung.

'You could have done a cordon bleu course if you'd wanted. It was you who wanted to do that MBA and have a career in banking. Daddy would much rather have had a proper wife who made food look nice.'

'So much for the feminist influence in the younger generation,' muttered Rachel. 'Stop nagging, you little reactionary. Your father wanted me to have the chance to do work that interested me. Just as he wanted you to,' she added with point.

Before his last session in hospital, Brian had mounted a fierce campaign so that Alexandra could study the physics course she'd wanted rather than the biology course that had suited the school curriculum. He had won. It had been good to see his triumph, especially as Alexandra had been delighted with the defeat of authority in the shape of her formidable headmistress.

Reminded now, Alexandra looked uncomfortable. Rachel pursued her advantage ruthlessly. 'By the way, how is school going?'

Alexandra regarded her beadily. 'If you're asking whether I've done my homework, the answer's yes.'

'I wasn't, actually. If I wanted to know the state of your homework, I would ask,' Rachel said levelly.

She reached for the gardenia-scented hand cream which Alexandra had bought her for Christmas when they'd still been in relative harmony—before Theo had appeared. She began to smooth it over her fingers. The potato water had given them the texture of old prunes.

'It just occurs to me that I've got to go to your PTA meeting next week. I could do with some advance briefing.'

Alexandra watched. Eventually she burst out, 'You mean you actually think you'll get there this time?'

This was an unexpected attack. Rachel gaped.

'I've only missed one,' she protested. 'I couldn't help that. The Malaysian deal. I told you.'

'Two others,' corrected Alexandra. 'The one before Christmas—you said it was only a social. And then Hugh's last one.'

'I didn't. I—' Rachel stopped, remembering. She grew indignant. 'The plane was late. I got there in the end.'

'Not in time. Hugh particularly wanted you to talk to Mr Templeton about him doing Russian and Mr Templeton had gone.'

'I talked to his tutor,' said Rachel defensively.

'His tutor's a silly old prat who thinks clever boys do Greek, not Russian,' said Alexandra, with her usual grasp of essentials. 'Hugh needed you to tell him to bog off. You didn't and now he's lumbered.'

One of Alexandra's great strengths as a tactician was to point out the genuine shortcomings of the adults in her life. While they were feeling properly guilty, they forgot the substance of their original argument. Rachel reminded herself of this.

'I'll talk to Hugh about it,' she said.

Alexandra looked annoyed. But she was shrewd enough to recognise that her move had been countered. She shrugged.

'So how *is* school going?' said Rachel, returning with an effort to the subject in hand.

For a moment Alexandra seemed almost uncomfortable. Then she said airily, 'Oh, boring. But I survive.'

'Well, congratulations.' Rachel's tone was dry. 'Now tell me the truth.'

Alexandra sent her a look of dislike. 'What has Gilly been saying?'

Trained by experience, Rachel concealed her surprise. She raised her eyebrows. 'What do you think?'

'She promised she wouldn't split,' said Alexandra with disgust. She glowered but decided to expand. 'It's nothing. I just told the Hornbeam I wasn't wasting my time doing stupid maps for history prep.' She snorted. 'You'd think we were five instead of fifteen. Tracing paper and coloured pens at our age. I ask you.'

'I see.' Rachel folded her lips together in an attempt to curb instinctive laughter. On the whole she was successful. 'And what did Mrs Hornbeam say?'

Alexandra shrugged. 'Stamped and screamed and threatened thumbscrews,' she said indifferently.

Rachel nodded. 'I see. Standard stuff.' She took some more hand cream and applied it absorbedly. 'And how did it happen to come to Gilly's notice?'

'Oh, Susanna didn't do her map-making either. The Hornbeam told Gilly I was a bad influence.'

This seemed to afford Alexandra considerable satisfaction. Rachel comforted herself with the fact that Susanna's parents could not share the form mistress's opinion or they would not be allowing their daughter to spend all her free time with Alexandra. She put down the bottle of gardenia hand cream with resolution, however.

She said carefully, 'You and Susanna are growing up. You need your personal space, I know. And you can do without people like me telling you how to run your personal relationships. I accept that. But when you're young—'

The doorbell rang. Alexandra had been beginning to look mulish but the sharp ring wiped the frown off her face. She stopped even pretending to listen to Rachel.

'Theo,' she said, her face lighting up.

'You can make mistakes that take so much getting over, it's out of all proportion to the fun you had in the first place.'

But Alexandra had already flown to the door. After a moment, Rachel gave a twisted smile. She was not entirely sorry. If Alexandra had been listening she would have demanded an explanation. Rachel was not sure that she had one. Not without explaining Riccardo di Stefano. She did not think she could bear that. Surely there was a limit on the self-immolation required of a stepmother?

CHAPTER SEVEN

RACHEL sighed and followed in her stepdaughter's wake, bracing herself to give stern warning on being home before eleven. It was not needed. It was not Theo Judd on the doorstep. It was the only visitor who was more unwelcome.

'Rachel,' purred Riccardo di Stefano, stepping past an open-mouthed Alexandra and taking both Rachel's hands in his. 'So good to see you relaxed at last.'

It was like a nightmare, Rachel thought. She was utterly unprepared. She had no arguments to get rid of him and no possible excuse for leaving the house herself. In her jeans, with the rumble of the washing machine behind her and the kitchen full of the smell of Gilly's good stew, it was obvious that she had settled down for a family evening at home.

Riccardo assessed the situation in a moment. He discarded his well-cut overcoat and dropped it over an oak chair in the hall. Alexandra followed, her eyes wide.

'How pleasant,' he said, sniffing the aroma of hot food with appreciation.

He strolled into the kitchen with the ease of an accustomed guest. You would think that he was not only invited but absolutely certain of his welcome, thought Rachel indignantly. Such was his confidence that she gave ground before him. She retreated behind the kitchen table. He gave a small nod, as if that was what he'd expected.

'I was going to take you out to dinner,' he announced. 'But that would clearly be redundant.'

Rachel braced herself against a kitchen chair. The warm wood was reassuring somehow.

She said arctically, 'If you remember, I refused.'

Alexandra swung between them, looking intrigued.

'And now I see why,' he said politely.

Alexandra did not like being ignored. She said, 'Rachel didn't cook that.'

Rachel ignored her stepdaughter. She was concentrating all her force on Riccardo. She was shaking imperceptibly—with temper. She assured herself it was temper.

'You know perfectly well why I refused to have dinner with you.'

'Do I?'

'Just as you did at the time. Which is why you turned up here, isn't it?'

Riccardo's eyelids dropped. 'Maybe.'

'Rachel can't cook at all,' Alexandra told him chattily. 'Well, only scrambled eggs and baked beans.'

Riccardo directed a slow smile at Rachel. She could feel the heat of it, like a furnace, like sunshine. Nine years ago, a look like that would have set her blushing furiously. What was it Judy had said? She was an open book? Rachel thanked God for experience and kept her complexion. Riccardo's smile widened.

'Then it's just as well it's not her cooking I'm interested in, isn't it?' he said, not taking his eyes off Rachel.

Alexandra was impressed. Rachel was outraged.

She said crisply to her stepdaughter, 'Mr di Stefano is a business acquaintance.'

Alexandra did not look convinced. Riccardo's attitude did not help. He shook his head reproachfully.

'Business acquaintance? Do you feel that covers it?'

'Yes,' said Rachel hardily.

He put his head on one side, consideringly. 'I would say our relationship is a little more—complicated than that.'

Rachel forgot their audience. She forgot boardroom diplomacy and her beloved career as well. All she was aware of was a great need to tell him exactly where she stood. She met his eyes, her own cold as glass.

'We have no relationship.'

Alexandra, enthralled, held her breath.

Riccardo was not put out in the slightest. 'If that were true I would not be here.'

Rachel gave him a look of undisguised dislike. 'Well, I certainly didn't invite you and I can't think of any reason why you should be here.'

'Can't you?'

She set her teeth. 'Mr di Stefano—'

'Riccardo.'

She ignored that. 'I don't want to be rude—'

'Don't you?' He looked amused.

Rachel ignored that too. She swept on. 'This is my home. I try not to bring work home. I don't always succeed. But I don't encourage colleagues to turn up on the doorstep unannounced. You, if you will forgive me, are—however grand—just another colleague.'

He did not like that. She could see it from the way his face went very still. All vestige of amusement was banished. Suddenly, he looked the ruthlessly successful man she knew him to be.

'More than that, I think,' he corrected her quietly.

It was not—quite—a threat. Rachel went white. She folded her arms quickly across her breast, hugging her waist. Her face felt pinched. Alexandra, she saw, was looking uncharacteristically shocked, and uncertain. Rachel tried to pull herself together.

'We'd do better to discuss this in private,' she said through stiff lips.

Riccardo was not given to remorse. His eyes flicked over Alexandra at last. He looked back at Rachel.

'Quite,' he said blandly.

Rachel decided that she hated him.

The doorbell rang again. This time Alexandra did not dive for it at once. She was chewing her lip, regarding Riccardo with dawning suspicion. She had also shrunk rather closer to her stepmother. Rachel felt sorry for her.

'That will be Theo, won't it?' she said gently.

'Yes.' Alexandra hesitated, still undecided.

'Then you'd better let him in. You invited him.'

'I know. But—'

The bell rang again, insistently. Reluctantly, Alexandra went off to the front door. Left alone, Riccardo and Rachel measured each other like duellists.

He said softly, 'She's very protective.'

'She's very young,' said Rachel sharply.

'But not young enough to be your daughter.'

Her head came up. 'What?'

He said in a musing voice, 'Marriage to a man old enough to be your father. Two adolescent stepchildren. Full responsibility for them when he dies. Plus a demanding climb up the corporate ladder. Don't you ever feel out of your depth?'

Her eyes glittered. 'Do you?'

For a moment he looked taken aback. 'I direct my own course.'

'So do I.'

His brows rose. She thought he was going to challenge her. But then Alexandra came back into the kitchen with Theo and the moment passed.

Theo, as usual, was wearing a black leather jacket and dark jeans that Alexandra, no doubt, thought the height of sophistication. As always he was so much at ease that Rachel wanted to hit him. It deflected her momentarily from Riccardo di Stefano.

'Hi, Mrs Gray. How you doing?'

'Fine, thank you,' said Rachel with restraint. 'You?'

'Can't complain.' He eyed Riccardo di Stefano. 'You want us out, right?'

'No,' said Rachel.

'Perceptive of you,' said Riccardo at the same time.

Theo grinned. 'No sweat. We're on our way.' He flicked a forefinger in Alexandra's direction. 'Get waddling, doll.'

Rachel closed her eyes, anguished. Alexandra, however, found nothing to complain of in this mode of address. She grabbed a crocheted shawl, swung it about her shoulders and flung her arm round Theo's waist. She was positively luminous with glee.

'Ready.'

'Back by eleven,' Rachel reminded her.

Alexandra frowned but the curfew clearly suited Theo very well.

'You're on,' he said. 'Eleven it is.'

They began to go.

'Have a good time,' said Rachel, though it cost her.

Theo gave her an altogether too knowing look over his shoulder. 'We will.'

The front door slammed. Rachel let out a long breath of relief. No longer obliged to contain her frustration, she picked up an oven glove and threw it hard at the opposite wall.

Di Stefano considered the fallen thing with some amusement. 'Don't like the boyfriend?'

Rachel was reminded that she hated Riccardo more than she loathed Theo Judd. 'That's got nothing to do with you.'

'That depends on your point of view.'

She sent him a look of dislike and went round the table to pick up the oven glove. Di Stefano forestalled her. He picked it up and tossed it absently onto the table behind her. Then he took her gently by the arm.

Rachel froze.

'From where I'm sitting, anything that comes between you and your work has rather a lot to do with me,' he said quite gently.

His hand was incredibly warm on her bare arm. It set up a perceptible flutter in her throat. Rachel ignored it, trying to disengage herself.

She said icily, 'Nothing comes between me and my work.'

He did not let her go. 'That's not the way I hear it.'

'What?' She was so startled that she stopped pulling against those imprisoning fingers.

'Philip tells me that you have been very preoccupied recently. He thought—trouble at home. Of course, you're very young to have such a big responsibility. He assumed it was getting you down.'

Riccardo's tone was neutral. He expressed no opinion; he was merely reporting an allegation, awaiting her response. It was all admirably unemotional.

Rachel was unable to match that professional impassivity. She shook herself free from his grasp.

'If that were true, why didn't Philip say anything to me about it?'

Riccardo shrugged. 'Didn't want to add to your burdens?' he suggested indifferently.

'Balderdash. Philip doesn't know a single thing about my burdens. And cares less,' said Rachel roundly.

There was quick gleam of triumph in the dark eyes. It was as quickly masked but Rachel had seen it. It set light to all sorts of vague suspicions.

She said slowly, 'When did Philip tell you he thought I had trouble at home?'

Riccardo had the grace to look uncomfortable. 'He didn't exactly tell me—'

'When?' Rachel was implacable.

'I called him this evening,' he admitted.

'You called him? About me?'

If she thought he would show any sign of decent confusion she was disappointed.

'Naturally.'

She was so outraged that for a moment she could barely speak. 'How dare you?' she managed at last.

'If we are to trust the recovery program to you, I have to know that you are reliable. You are, after all, relatively inexperienced.'

Their eyes clashed. His mouth tilted wickedly.

'In banking, anyway.'

Rachel felt as if she had been hit. Her head reared up. For a moment the kitchen seemed to swing wildly about her. She almost staggered. Something flickered in those strange eyes and he reached out as if to steady her.

This time she had no trouble at all in detaching herself. She shook his hand off as if it were no more than a troublesome insect. She held his eyes with hers.

'I see,' she said softly.

His eyes narrowed. 'What do you see?'

'You think you have some sort of special influence over me.'

'Not influence.'

She paid no heed to his protest. 'Because I knew you when I was young and silly, you think you can walk into my life and hijack whatever part of it happens to amuse you at the moment.'

His face tightened. 'Don't be melodramatic.'

She brushed that aside too. She took an angry step towards him. 'I've got news for you. I grew up.'

'I noticed.'

'I'm not so easily intimidated. Not any more.'

His look was frankly incredulous. 'Are you trying to say you were intimidated the last time we met?'

Rachel set her teeth. 'The last time we met,' she said with precision, 'I was eighteen years old.'

To her astonishment, Riccardo di Stefano looked away. A faint colour ran along the high cheekbones. Could the man possibly be embarrassed?

He said stiffly, 'So I have been told.'

'So don't think you can treat me like a child any more. I've learned a few things along the way, including how to fight my corner.'

The flush—if a flush it had been—was gone. It left him surprising pale under the accustomed tan. 'I am sure you have. But you don't have to fight me.'

'Don't I?' said Rachel. It was a challenge and neither of them pretended anything else.

Riccardo muttered something under his breath. It sounded explosive and uncharacteristically agitated. He pushed a hand through his hair.

'Rachel, I didn't come here to fight with you.'

She could see herself reflected in the mirror that hung on the wall behind his head. Her eyes were too bright, like those of a child who had been too long at a party. She thought, I've got to get him out of here.

She said, 'No, you came here to remind me about an episode which was over and done with nine years ago.

I don't know if you think that puts me in your power in some way. I can only tell you that it does not. Nor does it give you any right to invade my private life—'

He held up a hand, quite suddenly. He was smiling but Rachel had the sudden impression that he was very angry.

'Any invading,' he said, too quietly, 'was done a long time ago and was entirely mutual.'

Rachel snorted. 'Don't be ridiculous.'

'It is not ridiculous. It is the truth. As you would recognise if you would only stop spitting for a moment and talk this over like a reasonable person.'

'I am not,' said Rachel with the calm of despair, 'going to stand here discussing my adolescent disasters with you.'

He homed in at once on the one word that gave her away. She would have recalled it if she'd been able to. But it was too late.

'Disasters?' He took a step forward.

Rachel backed. 'I hate post-mortems.'

Another step forward. She had nowhere else to go unless she swung herself backwards into the sink.

'Why disasters?'

She lifted her chin and met his eyes with as much dignity as she could muster.

'Don't be disingenuous, please. Of course it was a disaster. One night with the last of the all-time playboys? It had to be a disaster.'

He drew in a little breath as if she had punched him unexpectedly. But it did not stop that slow advance on her position. He was now so close that she had to strain back not to touch him. A muscle worked in his cheek.

'I see your point,' he admitted levelly. 'What I don't see is why.'

He put a hand on her waist. It felt hot, burning. Suddenly Rachel was having trouble getting her thoughts together.

'Why?' she echoed.

Another step. No amount of craning backwards could avoid physical contact now. He touched her everywhere—thigh, hip, shoulder. He towered over her, making her look up into his face. It was quite without expression.

'Why it had to be just one night,' he explained.

Rachel stared at him. Desperately she reminded herself that, however practised he was, she had the measure of him. These days she could meet him on his own ground and rout him. Had she not been training herself to do exactly that for the last nine years?

But the last nine years seemed to be dancing away from her. Looking up at him, she could almost smell the ocean again, hear the distant rock band and, closer, the whirr of the old-fashioned ceiling fan above their heads. She swallowed.

Riccardo said, quite kindly, 'You made a mistake leaving like that.'

'L-leaving?'

'I said we'd talk in the morning. I don't like waking up and finding the lady I should be having breakfast with has gone.'

Some vestige of common sense reasserted itself. Rachel gave a crack of cynical laughter. 'Tough.'

He smiled but his eyes were veiled. 'It was. Oh, it was. Especially as we had not done with each other. Had we?'

Rachel reared back, shocked. Riccardo laughed aloud. He touched a finger to her mouth. It was hardly a touch, just a butterfly brush of the very tip of his finger, but it made Rachel shake visibly as if he had branded her.

He saw her reaction and smiled. 'We are not done yet, are we?'

She might be shaking but she had built some defences in the last nine years. Now, at last, she activated them. She pushed at him, head down, outraged. 'Get out of my house.'

He gave ground, his eyes alight with laughter suddenly. 'Are we?'

'Out.'

She drove him back through the kitchen, the hall. He went, throwing up his hands like a defeated duellist. But he did not look defeated. He looked alert and interested and altogether too cool.

'There's unfinished business between you and me, Rachel. You know it and so do I. Nothing either of us can say will change that.'

'Get out. *Now.*'

He shrugged. 'If not now, later.'

Rachel picked up his coat and flung it at him. He caught it one-handed, hesitated for a second, then reached out and took her chin in one long-fingered hand. Rachel let out a screech of sheer animal rage.

And Riccardo di Stefano leaned forward and kissed her hard on the lips. He did not wait to see her reaction.

The next day Rachel was waiting for Philip when he came into his office at nine. He was surprised but he showed no sign of an uneasy conscience.

'Good morning, Rachel,' he said, regarding his personal computer with disfavour. He sighed and turned it on. 'Jolly well done yesterday, by the way. I didn't get the opportunity to say so at the time. Rick was most impressed.'

'I just bet he was,' said Rachel grimly.

'What?' Philip looked up from the keyboard he was squaring up to gingerly. 'Sorry, missed that.'

She sat down on the end of the sofa which Philip kept for his most illustrious clients. Her mind went blank.

It was odd. Rachel had thought out this interview so carefully. When she had told Gilly that she was going to appeal to her colleagues' egos, it had been of Philip that she'd been thinking. She had thought she could get him on her side by showing him a way to score a victory over di Stefano. After yesterday he would be badly needing to do something to restore his self-esteem. Last night she had concocted a strategy step by step.

This morning it was gone. Rachel looked down at her hands and desperately tried to recall what had seemed so obvious last night. She tried to think of a way to approach the subject subtly. Nothing came. In the end she blurted it out baldly.

'I need to know what di Stefano said. About me, I mean.'

As soon as she'd said it, she could have kicked herself. It was about the worst thing she could have thought of. Instead of getting Philip on her side, it immediately set him on the defensive.

He bridled. 'Well, we had other things to talk about. Business strategy in the wider arena—'

There was no point in playing games. Rachel cut him short. 'Not about the bank. Me. Personally. Look, Philip, I ought to tell you—' She broke off, biting her lip.

In the coldest watches of the night, telling Philip what had happened nine years ago had seemed logical. Indeed, it had seemed the only thing to do. As long as she was trying to hide it, Riccardo had the upper hand. He, as he had made perfectly clear, did not care who knew. No, the only sensible thing to do was to tell Philip and trust his discretion.

As she was now finding out, however, it was one thing to reach a reasoned conclusion in the small hours, but quite another to carry it out. She found she was twisting her hands together and straightened her fingers quickly.

'Tell me what?' prompted Philip.

'Oh, this is horrible,' she burst out. 'This is exactly what they always say women executives do—mess up business with feelings. And it's so unfair.'

Philip looked at her in the liveliest astonishment. He even stopped playing with the keyboard.

'My dear Rachel. *Feelings?*' He looked as if he could not believe his ears. 'Is anything wrong?'

Rachel fought for composure. She smoothed her skirt with hands that shook slightly.

'I'm sorry,' she said quietly after a pause. 'I didn't mean to get emotional. I won't again.'

Philip's astonishment was comical. *'Emotional? About Rick di Stefano?'*

Rachel frowned, not understanding. Then she realised that Philip was thinking she was much too dull and businesslike to get involved with his demon shareholder. In spite of the horrors of the previous day, Rachel gave a choke of laughter.

It made her feel better. She sat up straight and told him an edited version of the truth. You could see that Philip found even the expurgated version difficult to believe.

'A—er—flirtation?' he said, torn between honest fascination and the English gentleman's code which regarded all reference to feeling as a serious breach of good taste.

'I was very young.'

'Yes, of course. You must have been. So that was why—' He broke off. 'Oh, what's the point? I've never been any good at hiding things. He was in here last night demanding to look at the personnel files.'

Rachel felt slightly sick. 'You didn't—?'

'No.' Philip was quietly proud of himself. 'I told him the bank had a duty of confidentiality to its employees. But I didn't see any harm in giving him your CV. Damn it, Rachel, it's practically a public document since you gave that interview to *Women on the Ladder*.'

Rachel had to admit that was so.

'He was spitting mad,' Philip said thoughtfully. 'I thought it was because we had employed someone so young to do such a crucial job. But it wasn't, was it?'

Rachel swallowed. 'I don't think so, no.'

'It was personal.'

'I don't see why it should be, but—' She shrugged.

Philip looked uncomfortable. 'Well, if you—er—turned him down... Men don't forget that, you know.'

'Surely he's been turned down often enough since then?' said Rachel, startled into indiscretion. 'It can't be that big a deal.'

'It's always a big deal,' said Philip drily, forgetting the English gentleman's code completely. 'Probably worse if you've got a track record like Rick di Stefano's.'

He thought about it for a moment, his kindly face sober. Then he said, 'I think you need to take care, Rachel. Rick obviously hasn't forgotten and he might want to make you pay. I'd keep out of his way, if I were you.'

She was careful not to let her relief show. 'Do you think I can?'

Philip waved an airy hand. 'Of course. He's only here till Thursday, then he's flying back to New York. All you have to do is keep out of the office. There's the project in Aberdeen. Go up and see how the site evaluation is coming along. Don't come back till Friday.' He gave her a sudden conspiratorial grin which reminded her why she liked working with him so much. 'That will settle him.'

So in the end her strategy worked, even though she had not played her own part quite as she had written it. Rachel walked out of Philip's office not knowing whether to laugh or to be thoroughly ashamed of herself. It was not Philip's ego that had come down on her side; it was his kindness of heart.

The moment she got back to her own office suite, however, she stopped worrying over the ethical point. The place was full of exotic flowers. So full, in fact, that it looked more like a botanical greenhouse than a place of work.

Rachel stopped dead in the doorway and shaded her eyes.

'Mandy, are you in there?'

Her secretary's voice floated out from Rachel's private office. 'Coming.'

She emerged carrying a woven basket of rushes and big waxy flowers. Rachel quailed. 'Do they bite?'

Mandy chuckled. 'Wouldn't be surprised. You should see the instructions that come with them.'

Rachel looked round, feeling helpless. 'What on earth is going on here?'

'Well, he either thinks we should make a bid for Kew Gardens and is starting you off on the acquisition research or he fancies you,' Mandy said calmly.

'He?' echoed Rachel, her heart sinking.

'Riccardo di Stefano.'

'Oh.'

She sank limply onto a chair, found it was occupied by a basket of assorted foliage, and propped herself against the wall instead.

'He's been on the phone too,' Mandy informed her helpfully.

'Oh,' said Rachel again.

She moved the chunky basket to the floor and sat on the chair. Mandy wedged the rushes into the window-sill and turned. She folded her arms across her and considered Rachel.

'Are you going to tell me?' she asked pleasantly. 'Or do you just want me to speculate wildly like everyone else in the building?'

Rachel shook her head helplessly. 'You can't be speculating any more wildly than I am. I don't know what the hell he's playing at. Why all this?' She spread her hands.

'Didn't he say last night?' asked Mandy artlessly.

Rachel stiffened. 'Last night?'

'I know he got your address out of Philip. Joan was worried about it.' Joan was Philip's secretary. 'But by that time there was nothing much she could do. We thought about phoning you.'

'What made you decide against it?' said Rachel bitterly.

Mandy was apologetic. 'It seemed like we were over-reacting a bit, when we got to talk it through. I mean he wasn't going to do anything dramatic, was he?' She looked round the exotic plant collection doubtfully. 'At least, we thought he wasn't,' she ended on an uncertain note.

Rachel took pity on her. 'Don't worry. He didn't.' She prodded a yucca plant distastefully. 'At least, not until this morning. What on earth are we going to do with the plant life?'

'Leave it to me,' Mandy said. 'One each to everyone on the Christmas Social committee. That will get rid of them.'

Rachel looked at her with awe. 'You're inspired.'

'All part of the service.'

'They don't have to take them home today. The plants can stay here till the end of the week. I'm going up to Aberdeen. I won't be back in the office until Monday.'

Mandy nodded in comprehension but she did not make any other comment. She reached for her pad and made a note.

'Do you mind which flight you take?'

Rachel grimaced. 'The later the better, I suppose. I don't have much packing but I need to make arrangements for the kids.'

Mandy added the information to her notes. 'Hotel?'

'Whichever the others are staying in.'

'Fine. I'll get onto it.' She peered round a spray of orchids to read her PC screen. 'You're seeing Mr Torrance at ten—did you remember?'

'Yes. Thank you.'

Mandy looked up, her eyes crinkling in amusement. 'And do you want me to get Mr di Stefano for you before or after your meeting?'

Rachel snorted. 'After the next ice age for preference.'

'He'll call again before then,' Mandy said sapiently. 'What do you want me to do about that?'

Rachel was conscious of the beginnings of a headache.

She sighed. 'If he calls I'll speak to him. But you'd better warn him that I'm on my way out of town.'

'I'll do that,' promised Mandy. Her expression said that she did not think much of it as an evasion tactic.

In that she was wrong. Colin Torrance came and went and there was no message from di Stefano. Thereafter, Rachel steamed through her in-tray at a rate of knots and heard the telephone ring in the outer office several times. But no call was put through to her.

It was, she thought, half-annoyed, half-amused, oddly frustrating. She did not want to have to talk to him. After last night there was nothing she wanted less. But she was left with the unpleasant feeling that it was inevitable at some point and that she was just marking time while she waited for the axe to fall.

In the end she could bear it no longer. She flung down the pen with which she had been doodling for ten minutes and went out to Mandy's office.

'Er—messages?'

Mandy looked up, unsurprised. She gestured at the screen in front of her. 'They're in the postbox.'

'Ah.'

Rachel still lingered in the doorway. Mandy took pity on her.

'Di Stefano wouldn't leave a message. He said he'd catch you later.'

'Ah,' said Rachel in quite a different tone. She looked at her watch. 'I think I'll take an early lunch. You don't know when I'll be back.'

In the reception hall the security guard opened the door for her.

'Your car's waiting, Mrs Gray.'

Rachel stared. 'My car?'

'Chauffeur came in to say he'd wait on the corner until he was moved on. Been there about twenty minutes.'

Rachel shook her head. 'Not my car, Geoff. Maybe Mr Jensen's?'

Geoff was unconvinced. 'It was you he asked for.'

An explanation occurred to her. 'Maybe Mandy ordered a car to take me to the airport this evening. They must have got the pick-up time wrong. I'll have a word. Thanks, Geoff.'

But when she went to the corner the vehicle was not her usual hired car with a friendly driver she knew but a dark-windowed limousine. The man who got out wore full chauffeur's uniform, including leather gloves. Gloves! Rachel goggled.

The chauffeur showed no emotion. Impassively, he opened the rear nearside door and stood to attention. It was quite clear that he knew who she was.

'Good morning, Mrs Gray.'

'I think there's been some mistake. I didn't order a car.'

No reaction to that either. He simply stood there, like some flunkey waiting to take her to her coronation. Another suspicion presented itself.

'Perhaps you can tell me who did order the car?' she suggested affably.

'I do not have that information, madam.'

'Then let me guess. Di Stefano's private office?'

But the wooden face was not giving anything away.

'All right,' said Rachel. There was something exhilarating in the battle of wills. She was almost beginning to enjoy herself. 'Let's come at this from another angle. Where were you supposed to take me? I mean, you do know where to go, don't you? I don't just get the car and driver to go joyriding all over the Home Counties, wherever I want, do I?'

'My instructions are to drive you to St Thomas' Court.'

She frowned, sifting rapidly through her memory. It was not an address she knew. Briefly she wondered whether it was a hotel and was astonished that Riccardo would stay anywhere but the best hotel in London. Then it clicked into place.

'Chelsea. By the river, right? One of the apartment blocks at the harbour?'

The chauffeur unbent sufficiently to give her a stately nod in response to this.

So Riccardo di Stefano had decided to get her onto his own territory. His own *private* territory. While the harbour development was not exactly off the beaten track, it was hardly central either. Getting away from there could be complicated and time-consuming if she wanted to leave before he chose to let her go. She looked at the chauffeur assessingly.

'Are you also on stand-by to bring me back?'

He did not know. He was only given one instruction at a time. He did not know what his next job might be.

'Which means no,' interpreted Rachel.

She felt suddenly, gloriously angry. She had been spoiling for a fight all morning. Now, it seemed, it was being offered to her. She got into the car.

It took the chauffeur by surprise. It was a good few seconds before he collected himself sufficiently to close the door on her. He got into the driving seat and set the car in motion. They slid into the traffic.

As soon as they were on the Embankment and Rachel was satisfied that she could do so without distracting his attention dangerously, she leaned forward.

'I'd like to make a phone call, please.'

He unhooked the car phone from its stalk and passed it back to her. She dialled Mandy.

'Change of plan,' she told her crisply. 'Di Stefano sent a car. I seem to be lunching at St Thomas' Court in Chelsea.'

In front of her the chauffeur's shoulders stiffened. No doubt he would report back to di Stefano's private office.

Rachel hoped that he would. She hoped he would report verbatim.

To put a bit of ginger into his report, she said, 'No, it's not a kidnap *yet*. I don't intend that it shall turn into one either. If I'm not back by two, send a car out there to pick me up, will you?'

She handed the phone back to the chauffeur.

'Thank you.'

As she expected, the building was a tower. The chauffeur swept into a cordoned stopping-off area and helped Rachel alight. A uniformed attendant opened the security-coded door for her. He did not bother to ask her name. He clearly knew she was coming.

'Mr di Stefano is on the fourteenth floor,' he said kindly. 'Fine view.'

Rachel smiled, not committing herself. She paused, looking round the ultra-modern interior. It was cool and high, with an impressively glassed and domed entrance hall and elevators walled with coloured glass. If big money had a scent, it would smell like this, she thought: high-tech electronics overlaid with the scent of flowers out of their season and out of their natural habitat.

In fact, the entrance hall was full of enough plants to make a botanical-garden director jealous. At one end the source of all this vegetation was clear. It was a shop, small enough to call itself a boutique, large enough to house two very expensively dressed women. Orchids and Friends, it was called, and it lurked behind a dense hedge of jungle leaves. Rachel strolled over, to the confusion of the lift attendant.

'Can I help you?' said one of the women.

'I think you already have. Did you send a shipment to Bentley's Investment Bank this morning?'

'Bentley's? I don't think they're one of our clients. I can check, if you like.'

She did. She came back looking respectful—and a good deal more curious.

'Mrs Gray? Yes, we did. At the request of Mr di
Stefano. I'm sorry, did we forget to put in a card?'

'No,' said Rachel. 'Thank you.'

She turned back to the hovering attendant.

'All set for the fourteenth floor, then.'

He did not come up with her. He did not need to.
There was only one apartment on the fourteenth floor
and the lift did not open without a key. As soon as she
arrived, there was a little whirring sound, and the door
was flung open.

Expecting yet another uniformed flunkey, Rachel was
disconcerted to find herself face to face with the man
himself. He stood looking at her for a moment, his eyes
dark and unreadable.

'You came,' he said at last.

CHAPTER EIGHT

IT TOOK Rachel several moments to recover from her astonishment. She could not read Riccardo's expression. But, as the world rocked back into balance and became manageable again, she had the distinct impression that he felt he had won a battle. An important battle.

It made her furious. It also made her feel seriously uneasy.

Well, she had built a few defences in the last nine years, to say nothing of acquiring a whole range of social weapons. It had cost her, that armour. There were months when she went out into the world every day expecting to face an enemy. It had taught her self-reliance—and the ability to return fire with fire. What was the point of all that experience, if you did not use it?

So she gathered herself together, ignored the way her heart seemed to be shaking within her ribcage, and prepared to enter battle.

'What else could I do in the face of such a pressing invitation?' she said sweetly.

He laughed then, ushering her into the room with a mock bow. He did not pretend to misunderstand her.

'I know it was kind of dramatic. But what else could I do? You refused all my regular invitations.'

Rachel was feeling more in control than the previous evening. For one thing, she was dressed in her professional camouflage—dark suit, cream blouse, earrings. For another, by calling Mandy from the car, she had held her own against his underhand tactics. At least so far.

So she strolled in and looked around in a leisurely fashion, quite as if she had expected to come here for

136

ages and was not wildly unnerved by the events of yesterday. She even pretended to give his question serious
consideration.

'Well, I suppose you could have got yourself a mask
and broken into my room at midnight, like something
out of a silent movie,' she observed.

'Ouch,' he said, his expression wry.

Her smile got even sweeter, even deadlier.

'Or you could have done what civilised people do and
accepted that I do not want to go out with you.'

He flung back his head and laughed aloud at that.
'I'm not that civilised,' he told her.

'So I infer,' she said sharply.

She immediately regretted it. How was she going to
steer clear of dangerous subjects if she let him goad her
into sniping at him? From his complacent expression, it
seemed that Riccardo was thinking along the same lines.

So she did not join in his laughter or let her eyes meet
his. She did not get close enough for him to touch her
either. She swung sharply on her heel and went to the
long windows, well out of his reach. From the amused
silence behind her, she was pretty sure he knew exactly
what she was doing. For the moment, it seemed he was
prepared to go along with it. But for how long?

Rachel shivered, although the windows were closed.
They gave onto a balcony with a fine view of the Thames.
There was a marina below them. She remembered that
nine years ago he had been in the West Indies on a sailing
holiday.

She struggled to sound polite, neutral, utterly indifferent. 'Did you buy this place so you could moor your
yacht?' She only succeeded in sounding strained.

He looked amused. 'Not guilty.'

She was so startled that she did look at him then.
'What?'

'You've developed a fine curl of the lip since the last
time we met,' he explained. He strolled over to her side.
'It comes into play every time you mention me.' He

folded his arms across his chest and surveyed her. 'Tell me, Rachel, why do you disapprove of me?'

She had no immediate response to this head-on attack. 'I don't...' she began, floundering.

'Yes, you do. It shows. Even my staff have noticed.'

Rachel raised her eyebrows, returning gratefully to mockery. 'Your *staff*? That's bad.'

'I don't like it.'

The admission almost made her laugh aloud. But she primmed her mouth and tried to look solicitous. 'Image taking a beating, is it?'

'I think my credibility will survive a little longer.'

'Well, of course it will,' she congratulated him. 'It can't make that much difference that one insignificant clerk doesn't like working for you.'

He chuckled. 'Hardly insignificant. You pack quite a punch these days.'

'You flatter me. But I still don't think you or anyone else in your organisation gives a damn whether I'm happy in my work.'

He was still looking as if he was enjoying himself, damn him.

'You're a hard woman, Rachel.' He shook his head mournfully.

She pretended sudden enlightenment. 'Oh, *that's* the trouble. It's because I haven't fallen prostrate at your feet in adoration.'

His brows twitched together. Not enjoying himself quite so much now, thought Rachel. Their eyes clashed. Then he smiled, slowly, outrageously.

'Well, it's certainly got them talking,' he drawled.

Rachel gasped. She recovered at once. She did not like the implications of what he said but she was not going to admit it.

Instead she said with heavy irony, 'That must be a first.'

Riccardo sighed. 'Here we go again. Any minute now you're going to call me a playboy.'

A *playboy*? It did not begin to cover what she thought of him. But she was not going to be tempted into revealing her real feelings. Rachel turned away with a dismissive gesture.

Riccardo was not giving up. He turned her back to face him.

'No? Not a playboy? Or are you more tolerant of playboys these days?'

His hands on her made Rachel tense every muscle. You're in control, she reminded herself. He only sees what you let him. Don't give him a chance to see that he has any effect on you at all.

With an enormous effort of will she stood quiet in his hands. She even shrugged.

He shook her slightly.

'Talk to me, Rachel.'

Some of Rachel's careful indifference slipped.

'Take your hands off me,' she flashed.

His eyebrows rose, but he did not look exactly displeased. He stepped back and raised his hands comically, like a cowboy facing a toy gun.

'OK. OK. No touching. Just talk.'

She turned away, annoyed with herself. 'We have already talked.'

He shook his head slowly. 'I don't think so.' He hesitated. Then he said, as if he was choosing his words carefully, 'You're a key person in the team, Rachel. I can't afford to have you muttering behind my back.'

So that was it. She laughed angrily.

'Don't worry. I don't discuss my private opinions with colleagues,' she said curtly.

'That's not quite what I meant.'

She swung back on him. 'Nor do I lie about them.'

He frowned. 'Have I asked you to?'

Her chin came up. She braced herself for battle. 'If you don't like it—'

'I don't.'

'—then you'll just have to...' Rachel ground to a halt. 'What?'

'I don't like your opinion of me,' he said in his most reasonable voice. 'I want to find out why you feel the way you do about me. And then I want to change it.'

Rachel met his eyes and saw that he meant it. There was a short, shocked silence. Her burgeoning temper disappeared, to be replaced by something a lot more complicated.

She said breathlessly at last, 'You're not going to stay in London. We won't have to work closely. It can't be important.'

He just looked at her steadily, not speaking.

She said in exasperation, 'I don't see why you should give a damn what I think of you.'

'Don't you?'

'Some people just don't get on. It's chemistry or something.'

There was a pause.

Then he said quietly, 'Yes. I remember the chemistry.'

Rachel jumped. Her spine seemed to turn to rubber and go into free fall. She could not think of a thing to say.

'It was—quite something, as I recall.'

Rachel swallowed. 'Really.'

He looked down at her, his face serious. 'Are you saying you don't remember?'

Under that intense inspection, Rachel felt as if she could hardly breathe. She turned her face away. She managed a laugh. It sounded harsh. 'One night? Nine years ago?'

Riccardo's expression darkened. He began to drawl. 'Unlikely, I agree. But the circumstances alone made it memorable.'

'Not to me.'

His brows rose. 'You mean you turned it into a habit? Now, that does surprise me.'

Rachel did not trust herself to speak.

He said reflectively, 'I'd never done anything like that before.'

She snorted.

'You were an unknown quantity. A stranger. I'd always known all my girlfriends through and through. Just like they knew me.'

Rachel gave a nasty smile. 'You mean you both knew the limits of the deal. How convenient.'

To her astonishment, Riccardo's chin went up as if she had hit him. For a moment she thought she had penetrated that armour of his. But then the steep eyelids drooped to hide his expression.

'I couldn't have put it better myself,' he agreed lazily. 'I knew the terms of my deal. So tell me, what were yours?'

'Mine!' She was bitterly scornful. 'You're forgetting: I was too young to know about deals.'

'Yes?'

He was not showing a glimmer of conscience. His eyes were watchful. 'So what happened was purely spontaneous? No calculations? No prior research into the di Stefano millions? Just overwhelming attraction you couldn't run away from?'

Damn, thought Rachel. He had been leading her towards that damaging admission from the moment she'd walked in and she had not had the wit to see it. The silence screamed.

At last she said, 'I don't remember. I keep telling you, it's a long time ago.'

'You remembered enough to time your holidays from Bentley's in order to avoid me,' he pointed out.

There was no answer to that.

She tried to sound cool, logical. 'Well, of course, I remember what *happened*. I'm just not that certain what I felt.'

'No?' He was almost purring. 'Yet you said last night it was a disaster. An adolescent disaster, if I remember correctly.'

Rachel stared at him, hot-eyed. He was right, of course. Right and clever and utterly without compunction. She could have screamed. But under the anger a slow, horrifying sense of having been cornered by a master huntsman was seeping through her.

She broke away from that mesmerising gaze.

'I also told you last night I don't like post-mortems. What happened between you and me is ancient history and should be forgotten.'

'Have you forgotten?'

'I told you—'

'You told me a number of things,' said Riccardo di Stefano. 'Most of them contradictory. I don't think you know yourself what's true and what isn't any more. Or,' he added, suddenly grim, 'how much you've forgotten. Let's see, shall we?'

Rachel knew he was going to touch her. She knew she ought to move. But her muscles seemed to have locked. All she could do was close her eyes, to shut out that towering figure.

It was a mistake. A terrible mistake. With her eyes closed, she was back nine years in that quiet little room, listening to the old-fashioned fan, the cicadas outside, and their breathing.

This time she was wearing layers of sober cloth and a blouse that buttoned to the neck, not a disastrously tangled sarong. When his practised fingers drifted up her arm in a cruel imitation of love, they no longer encountered bare flesh.

It made no difference. The hurried sounds of their breathing were exactly the same. And she recognised in a flash of insight that Riccardo knew it too. He laughed under his breath.

'Same old instincts, I see.' His voice was not entirely steady.

This time it was not longing which hit Rachel. It was fear, naked and shocking. Her eyes flew open.

'Never again.' She almost screamed it.

The intensity of it shook both of them. He let her go. A blank look invaded his eyes. She stepped back, smoothing the dark sleeve of her jacket with fingers that shook.

'I'm sorry.' She sounded as shaken as she felt. 'I didn't mean to sound like a fishwife. I just meant...'

The blank look disappeared. It was replaced by cold anger. 'It was perfectly clear what you meant,' Riccardo said with bite.

Rachel swallowed. The anger beat at her, making her feel vulnerable and unsure. She shook herself. She might not have chosen to lose her cool and yell at him like that but, now that she had, at least it had made her point, she thought.

'Then perhaps you will accept that I mean what I say,' she said quietly.

He did not answer at once. His eyes flickered. His expression became an unreadable mask.

Eventually he said, 'I accept this is going to be...' he hesitated '...a challenge.'

It was, she could see, another piece of deliberate provocation. He was watching her clinically, like a scientist viewing an experiment, to see how she would respond. Rachel decided to surprise him.

'A short-lived challenge,' she said drily.

Riccardo raised his eyebrows. 'Because you're going to give in gracefully?'

'Because you're going back to New York this Thursday,' she pointed out sweetly.

Suddenly his expression was no longer a mask. His imminent departure must have slipped his mind in the heat of battle, Rachel thought, pleased. For a moment he looked furious.

'That is not—' He caught himself, biting off whatever he was going to say.

As if it had never been, the fury was gone. He lifted one shoulder in a negligent shrug that disclaimed any feeling at all. Rachel's eyes narrowed suspiciously. He saw it. His mouth tilted in appreciation.

He said solemnly, 'So I am. I'm really glad you reminded me.'

It was smoothly spoken but Rachel heard a threat in it. She backed off.

He sighed. 'No need to look like that. You've made your point. I concede.'

She looked at him warily. She did not believe him for a moment. Riccardo di Stefano was not a man to concede a fight unless it was part of a wider battle plan. The same battle. With her defences weakening all the time.

She almost jumped at the thought. Two days ago she would have said it was inconceivable that she could ever be tempted by Riccardo di Stefano again. Today she was honest enough to admit—to herself at least—that the temptation was still there. He looked at her, touched her—and she could feel her defences dissolving.

I must be *mad*, she thought. The sooner he went back to New York the better.

Unguarded, she said so. His lips twitched. She could feel the heat rising in her cheeks. But all he said was, 'Come and eat. The directors' kitchen has sent someone over. The food should be good.'

It was. It was also served by a formally suited waiter. At a stroke it destroyed the atmosphere of dangerous intimacy.

It was a relief. She told herself that it was an enormous relief. Unfortunately, a part of her was also disappointed. Because she had wanted to finish the fight, Rachel told herself. She did not quite believe it—and was furious with herself.

Riccardo adjusted smoothly to the presence of a third party. He seated her, plied her solicitously with wine and set about a social conversation that felt like an inquisition.

'Why banking?'

Rachel was struggling to hide her uneaten pasta under her cutlery. 'Bentley's were the first to offer me a job after my MBA.'

'All right, why a business degree? I know your father was a wheeler-dealer but I don't remember you being interested in business.'

'I don't remember you noticing what I was interested in,' flashed Rachel.

It did not take his satisfied smile to tell her she had made a mistake. She pushed irritatedly at her spaghetti carbonara.

He was too subtle to point it out, however.

She bit her lip and said with constraint, 'My father's company collapsed. I got used to listening.'

'Did you work with your father?'

Rachel found she could not face the spaghetti after all. She put down the forkful.

'No.'

'Why not?'

'Because... It's complicated.'

He leaned back in his chair, one casual arm resting on the table. 'I'm good at unravelling complications.'

Rachel shuddered at the thought of his unravelling this particular one.

'We had some difficulties,' she said briefly.

She saw him store away the information for future use.

'When did you meet Brian Gray?'

'I worked for him.'

He frowned. 'He was at Bentley's?'

Rachel hesitated. Did she want to tell him the truth? Would it lead him into further, more painful deductions? But in the end it seemed easier. She had not had enough practice to go on lying successfully if he asked further questions.

So she shrugged and told him unemotionally, 'No. Before my degree. After his first wife left, I worked for him as an au pair.'

Riccardo was frankly incredulous. 'An au pair?'

'He needed someone to look after the children. I needed a job and somewhere to live while I did my degree. It was ideal for both of us.'

He digested that. 'Was that why you married him? Mutual convenience?'

Rachel almost jumped. She looked round but the waiter had retired to the kitchen with their dirty plates.

She said carefully, 'We grew to know each other very well.'

He brooded.

'So when you married him you must have already known the children.' He looked up suddenly, his eyes like lasers. 'Fond of children, Rachel?'

'Not all children,' she said steadily.

'But these children? Alexandra and whatever-his-name-is? Fond of them, are you?'

'Of course.'

He nodded, as if that was what he'd expected. His voice was almost idle when he said, 'Fond enough to marry a man twenty years older than you so you could look after them?'

Rachel stared at the glass in her hand. Oh, Riccardo di Stefano was too clever. Too clever and too damned determined. He had a battle plan all right. It was going to take all her skill to get out of this one.

She put down her wine. 'Look, I'm sorry. I haven't much of an appetite and I really ought to be going. I need to pack.'

His eyes flickered at the information. Rachel was too perturbed to notice.

He said easily, 'Well, at least have a coffee before you go. Tell me about your delightful stepdaughter. What is wrong with the boyfriend?'

Rachel was relieved at the change of subject. This was one subject at least on which she could afford to tell the truth.

'Well, he's so much older—'

His look mocked her. She flushed but said hotly, 'At that age it's a big deal. He has no job and too much money. He gives her things all the time—'

'Ah,' he said. 'Very suspicious.'

It sounded like an accusation. She was taken aback. 'What?'

'Well, it's not really your style, is it, Rachel? Real women don't accept things from a man.' He gave a soft laugh but he did not really sound amused. 'Does it contaminate their independence irretrievably? You know, I think your stepdaughter has my sympathy.'

She stared. She sought for the reason for this veiled attack. A few moments' reflection gave it to her.

'Is this because I didn't say thank you for all those flowers this morning?' She got up and said without expression, 'Thank you. I was overwhelmed.'

He stood up too. His face was quite unreadable but the force of the movement sent his chair tipping over backwards behind him.

Rachel was suddenly afraid. It infuriated her. 'They weren't a gift. They were a message. You were telling the whole bank that you had the right to send me any damned thing you wanted. Well, now they know and my office looks like a jungle. Happy?'

'You are as original in your gratitude as you are in everything else,' he murmured.

Rachel snorted. 'I saw the florist you use as I was coming up. I suppose I should just be thankful you don't happen to have a chocolatier in your building, or my office would be a candy warehouse by now.'

This time the pause felt dangerous. Then, just as she was bracing herself to turn and run for the lift, Riccardo burst out laughing.

'Oh, Rachel, what a firebrand you are. You can find more reasons to start a fight than any woman I know.' He seized her hand and held it between both of his. 'Yes, I know—you want to go. I won't stop you. This time.'

She felt the warmth of his palm, the strength of his fingers... A little bit more of her defences fizzed and disappeared. Rachel tugged her hand away.

'Goodbye.' She meant to sound decisive and in control. She did not. Even to her own ears she sounded on the edge of panic.

But he let her go easily enough.

He said, 'Not goodbye. You can't expect to have it all your own way.'

Rachel was turning away. She looked back at that. 'I don't know what you mean.'

The smile he gave her was caressing. 'You start the fights, darling. Leave me to finish them.'

CHAPTER NINE

RICCARDO'S words stayed with Rachel all afternoon. She raced through her work and dashed home to pack. She turned the radio up high but it did not drown out that amused, determined voice.

What had he meant? Rachel tried to convince herself that he'd meant nothing, that he had just been trying to worry her. But she could not. She might not have seen Riccardo di Stefano for nine years but in some ways she knew him as well as she knew herself, she thought. She knew he did not make empty threats.

She tried to put it out of her mind. She had to talk to Alexandra and she needed her whole mind on the conversation.

She picked her up from school. Alexandra got into the car. She was evidently torn between satisfaction at getting a lift on a rainy day and wariness.

'Girl talk?' she demanded suspiciously, lobbing her bag into the back seat.

Rachel concentrated on pulling the car out of the double-parked whirlwind outside the crowded school gates.

She chose her words with care. 'Not unless you want to.'

Alexandra shook back her hair defiantly. 'If you think you can talk me out of seeing Theo, you can think again.'

Rachel did not rise to that one.

'I've talked to Mother,' Alexandra announced. 'She says she doesn't see anything wrong with it.'

'Well, that's a body-blow for me,' said Rachel gravely.

Alexandra bit back a snort of laughter. 'She *is* my mother.'

'And she doesn't know Theo.'

The atmosphere chilled perceptibly.

'Nor do you. He's got a lot of potential. It's just that people are prejudiced against him.'

Rachel groaned. 'Don't tell me. The world doesn't understand him.'

'Oh, you're so cynical,' burst out Alexandra. 'Why can't you give people the benefit of the doubt, try being open-hearted for once?'

Rachel thought about her interview with Riccardo di Stefano. She had hardly been open-hearted there. On the other hand, that was the legacy of painful personal experience. Were you supposed to chuck out what you had learned and pretend that people were trustworthy when you had serious evidence that they were not?

She said sadly, 'Maybe I am. Maybe your way is better. Perhaps if you trust people to behave well even the worst of them can rise to the occasion.'

She felt Alexandra staring at her. Rachel could feel her astonishment. She drew a deep breath and launched into the speech she had been preparing all day.

She said quietly, 'Lexy, I have no right to give you advice. I haven't run my life well enough to think that I know better than you. But... Well, there was a time when I wasn't cynical enough. You probably won't believe it and I don't want to drag out all the gory details. But, believe me, it changed my whole life. Not for the better. I wouldn't want that to happen you.'

There was silence for a considerable time. Then Alexandra said in a small voice, 'Is that why you work all the time?'

It was Rachel's turn to be astonished. 'Do I?'

'More and more. Hugh says it's because you are so ambitious.' She ended on a faint note of query.

Rachel turned the car carefully onto the dual carriageway.

'And what do you think?'

Alexandra hesitated. Then she said slowly, 'There's a prefect at school. She's very clever. Always in the library. She used to go out with Nick Dorset. He ditched her after the school trip to France. Now she doesn't do anything except pass exams.'

Rachel caught her breath. At fifteen her stepdaughter was more perceptive than she had bargained for.

She said involuntarily, 'You're growing up.'

It was the wrong thing to say, of course. Hopelessly wrong. Alexandra was immediately insulted and said so.

'I *am* grown-up. Why won't you realise it? Does it push you over the hill, or something? Is that a problem for you? You don't respect me. You never have.'

The tirade went on until they reached home.

There were several messages on the answering machine—Mandy with the arrangements for her trip to Aberdeen, Gilly saying she would be delighted to have Alexandra to stay if she wanted, the cleaning lady promising to provide the children's evening meal. Alexandra listened, her face growing tighter and tighter. When the final beep announced the end of the tape she swung round on Rachel.

'You're going away,' she said tragically.

Rachel felt instantly guilty. 'Only until the weekend.'

'Why?'

'Work, I'm afraid,' she said, trying to forget that it also conveniently removed her from Riccardo's vicinity until he was safely on the plane back to his country.

'You don't care about us.'

'Of course I care.' Rachel's guilt was swamped by justifiable frustration. 'I'll be back in time to stop you going to the all-night rave with Theo,' she added.

Alexandra was not amused. She stamped. 'You're laughing at me. I *hate* you.'

She fled upstairs. Rachel sighed, shrugged and went to check her packing.

When Hugh came in, her bag was waiting in the hall and she was going through her briefcase. He stopped, swinging his schoolbag off his shoulders. He raised his eyebrows at the waiting luggage.

Rachel nodded. 'I'm afraid so. Only a couple of days this time. I'm back on Thursday night. Can you cope? Lexy can go to Gilly's if it's too much to ask.'

'She'll do her homework or I'll beat her,' said Hugh, grinding his teeth horribly. 'Of course I can cope. Lexy doesn't have fights with me.'

That was true. Rachel was still worried, though.

'If Theo turns up. . .'

Hugh's face closed. Suddenly he looked a lot older than his seventeen years.

'I can deal with Theo Judd. He won't try anything.'

'Well, if you have any trouble—'

'I'll lock Lexy in her room and plant a hedge of thorn-bushes,' he said impatiently. 'Don't worry. She's not as big a fool as you think she is.'

There was a swish of tyres, then an impatient honk from outside. The story of my life, thought Rachel.

She called upstairs, 'I'm off now, Lexy. Goodbye.'

There was no answer.

'I'll break it to her that I'm in charge,' Hugh offered.

Rachel hesitated, but she really did not have many options. She gave him a quick hug.

'You're a rock, Hugh.'

He hugged her back. 'Go for it, Killer.'

Rachel picked up her overnight bag and looped it over her shoulder.

'I'll call you from Scotland, let you have my number at the hotel.'

Hugh snapped her briefcase shut and opened the front door. He jerked his head at the door in a gesture of dismissal.

'Fine, if it makes you feel better. But nothing will happen.'

Rachel grimaced. She wished that had not sounded so much like a challenge to the gods. But she did not have time to discuss it further. Hugh put her briefcase in the car. He even permitted her to plant a brief kiss on his cheek as she got in.

'Don't *worry*.'

*   *   *

It was easy enough to say, thought Rachel as she settled onto her seat on the last shuttle of the day. Not so easy to put into practice. It was not that she did not trust them, she thought, but she saw how young they were, how vulnerable in their youth. How did you get that across without destroying their confidence completely, or else sounding paranoid?

She let her head fall back against the cushioned airline seat and closed her eyes. If only she could forget how it had hurt when her father had rejected her. She turned her head on the cushion restlessly. If only she could forget the even worse hurt: the weeks she'd waited when Riccardo had not come for her, the slow realisation that he was never going to come for her. She thought, What is wrong with me? I have not thought about this for years.

There was not much doubt why it had surfaced now and it was not Alexandra's behaviour. It was just something else to chalk up to Riccardo di Stefano's account.

She remembered his behaviour at lunch and set her jaw. I have made a good life for me and the children, she told herself. That is the thing to remember, not ancient history. No matter what Riccardo di Stefano says, there is no unfinished business between us.

She was still telling herself that when she emerged from the airport into a grey, windy evening. Rain was bouncing up from puddles. Rachel huddled the collar of her suit round her face, thinking bitterly that she would have refused to make this journey but for Riccardo. By the time she got to her hotel she was shivering as much from temper as the drenching.

'Mrs Gray?' said the pleasant uniformed girl at the desk. 'Yes, of course your room has been reserved. Will your husband be joining you?'

Rachel closed her eyes briefly. The girl might be pretty and efficient but she had a lot to learn in the way of tact.

'I doubt it,' she said with restraint. 'Tell Mr Torrance I've arrived when he comes in, will you, please?'

She found she had a huge room which was clearly part of a suite. The door to the adjoining room was locked. She bounced experimentally on the side of the enormous four-poster bed. When she sat on it, her feet did not touch the floor. Rachel stretched luxuriously, then grimaced as her jacket stretched clammily. Her suit was soaked.

The bath was the size of a ship. Fortunately there was more than enough hot water to fill it and the hotel helpfully provided small bottles of heather-scented oils and lotions. Rachel stripped off and sank back into scented steam.

'Thank God I packed a cocktail dress. I wonder how Colin would like to have dinner with a boss in a bathrobe?' she mused.

It was an entertaining thought. She chuckled, giving herself up to relaxation for the first time in what felt like days. Eventually her teeth stopped chattering.

The telephone on the wall rang.

'Hello?'

'Colin Torrance. Had a good journey?'

'I got wet.'

He laughed. 'We have a good bit of weather up here. Wait till you see the views, though. This place is spectacular in a storm.'

'I look forward to it,' said Rachel untruthfully. 'Downstairs in thirty minutes?'

She swirled her hair up in a towel, slid into the thick hotel robe that she was not going to have to wear for dinner and dialled home. Alexandra answered. Questioned, she admitted that she was finishing a history project which had to be given in the next day. Hugh took the phone from her.

'She's got books all over the floor and Susanna and Erica are here. They'll be lucky if they finish before dawn,' he said tolerantly.

'No Theo?'

'No.'

'Thank God,' said Rachel devoutly. She sent them all her love, promised to bring back the biggest box of shortbread she could find and rang off.

Her hair was too damp to pin up. She hesitated over using the hotel drier but she knew that it would only fluff her hair up uncontrollably. In the end she compromised, leaving it loose but pinning it back off her face.

She caught sight of her reflection and stopped, disconcerted. The red-gold waves reflected bronze lights from her smart cocktail dress. It made her look unexpectedly frivolous. Colin Torrance, she thought, would be astonished.

She went downstairs, pausing by the hotel manager's desk.

'I've left a suit hanging on the back of my door. It needs cleaning and pressing. Could you organise that, please?'

'Of course, madam. What room number, please?'

Rachel checked her keyring. Further down the lobby desk, the teenage enthusiast who'd signed her in was waving excitedly.

'Three-three-one,' Rachel said. 'Yes?' she added, to the receptionist.

'Mrs Gray, your husband called.'

That child needs more than lessons in tact, Rachel thought. She needs a brain transplant. She was about to say so when she saw Colin Torrance across in the bar.

So she contented herself with saying crisply to the girl, 'I don't think so,' before she went over to him.

He had been polite in her office but now he was positively effusive.

'It's a relief you're here,' Colin admitted. 'I can handle the lending but when it comes to the whole package—well—' He flung out his hands. 'They seem to think they've locked in the Far East orders, but I'm not so sure. And as for the currency risk—I don't think it's even occurred to them!'

'Why couldn't you say that in your report?'

He looked wry. 'We may be advising the company but there is a real power battle between father and son on the board. The last thing I want to do is get browbeaten into taking sides before I understand what's going on.'

'And the company is seeing the interim reports before you send them to head office?'

'Well, the board does.' Correctly sensing her annoyance, he added defensively, 'They insisted. It's in the contract.'

Rachel frowned. 'Heaven preserve me from companies who pay for advice they don't want. Presumably they think you're just up here to endorse one side or the other?'

He was philosophical. 'It's happened before. And Philip told me to keep the whole board sweet. We want that account.'

'Someone should tell Philip about logical impossibilities,' muttered Rachel. 'OK, give me a run-down on the personalities.'

Colin looked out of the window. Outside the rain was lashing at the window so hard that it was impossible to see across the road.

'Over dinner? I was thinking of taking you to a very good little Italian place but it might be better to eat here. It's very expensive and a bit—er—formal but we shouldn't have trouble getting a table on a night like this.'

Rachel shuddered at the thought of going out of doors again.

'Definitely here,' she said firmly. 'Bentley's can afford it.'

When they went into the dining room, however, she was taken aback.

'Formal? You have a gift for understatement, Colin.'

The tall Edwardian room had lowered its lights to the faintest of background glows. Illumination of the food was provided by candles in rose-decked candle-holders. The tables were covered with crisp linen and an Aladdin's treasury of glimmering goblets and silver. In one corner a pianist in a smoking jacket played Cole Porter by the light of a candelabra.

'Good grief,' said Rachel with feeling. She touched her bronze skirt as if it were a talisman. 'Do you realise that if my suit had not got soaked at the airport I would be seriously underdressed?'

Colin gave her a faint, uncomprehending smile. They were shown to a discreet corner table. The waiter whispered a welcome and presented them each with an enormous leather-bound menu. Rachel's had no prices. She began to feel an overwhelming urge to giggle.

'This place could give the Tunnel of Love a run for its money,' she said. 'Anyone sees us here and it's the end of your reputation. Probably mine as well. I thought seduction parlours like this went out in the naughty nineties.'

But Colin, a conscientious husband and father, did not see the funny side of it. He kept apologising for the room being too dark for her to read any of the papers he wanted to pass across the table to her.

'Give them to me later,' said Rachel impatiently. 'Just tell me your impressions so far.'

But Colin was worried about client confidentiality. He did not want to name names or say anything which could be overheard and correctly interpreted. As the dining room filled up he became increasingly agitated at the thought of industrial espionage by their fellow diners. In the end he resolved the dilemma by moving his seat to Rachel's right and murmuring about boardroom squabbles in her ear.

By the end of the meal it was not just the ponderously romantic ambience that was making it difficult for Rachel not to laugh. She almost snatched the papers from his hand when they left the dining room. She declined a final coffee in a choking voice and made for her room.

When she got there, she laughed until she cried. Eventually she sat up, wiped her smudged mascara and blew her nose.

Therapeutic, she decided.

For the first time in days she felt as if she could go to bed with a quiet mind. She undressed, brushed her hair until it jumped with static, and tumbled between deliciously laundered sheets.

'A good hotel,' she said drowsily, 'is halfway to paradise.'

It felt as if her head had hardly touched the pillow when she came out of her dreams with a jerk. She had been dreaming something fast and frightening. Her heart was still pounding as she fought her way back to consciousness. Once her eyes were open, though, she lost all memory of what it was that had frightened her.

She lay there, listening to the strange night sounds of the hotel. It made her feel oddly free. She had thrown back the curtains when she'd come in last night. Now she could see a distant streetlight and the pointed roof of a church, like a woodcut from a children's story book.

Somewhere out there, she thought lazily, there is the big shiny moon. She even toyed with the idea of getting up to look at it. But she was too comfortable. She plumped up her pillows and was beginning to turn over when something stopped her.

It was not a noise. Not a real noise. Not like voices in the corridor or tyres on the wet roads outside. Not even like a creaking door. It was more like a breath, as if some animal had managed to get into her room without her noticing.

Rachel was not afraid. But she was intrigued. She struggled up onto her elbow, listening.

Nothing.

But then her eyes accustomed themselves to the deep shadows in the room. She swivelled, inspecting the room. Door to the corridor. Big landscape on the wall. The picture was indistinguishable in the dark but the moonlight glinted off its protective glass, throwing off strange reflections. For a moment they looked almost like a man's shadow.

Rachel dismissed the fancy, letting her eyes travel on. Bathroom. Door to the adjoining room. Dressing table.

Chair. Heavy curtains pulled back to frame the night skyline. And she saw him.

He was standing behind the chair, as still as the unstirring curtains. As still as if he were the real occupant and somebody else the intruder. Now that she looked, Rachel could see that the door to the adjoining room was open behind him.

She stayed there, poised on her elbow, transfixed. She knew she ought to be frightened. She knew she was not.

She also realised that she knew who it was.

Slowly, she sat up. The dark silhouette made no move but she knew he had seen her movement. Her heart began to patter lightly, very fast, somewhere in the region of her throat.

She thought, I don't believe this.

The dark figure came towards her. He was a broad-shouldered outline against the uncurtained window. It was like a dream. A dream she had had many times, Rachel thought now—though she had never admitted it. There was no whirring ceiling fan, no distant hush and lull of the ocean, no cicadas. But everything else was familiar—wholly and heartbreakingly familiar.

He shrugged off his jacket. It fell to the floor. Revealed, his open-necked shirt gleamed white in the moonlight. That, too, was familiar. Rachel said nothing. She sank back among the pillows, watching.

She knew that he was looking at her. He unlinked his cuffs and pulled the shirt over his head, letting it fall unheeded to the floor. A faint fragrance reached her. It spoke of limes and the open air. Rachel swallowed. Suddenly it was suffocatingly difficult to breathe. She put a hand to her throat. He stopped, standing very still for a moment.

'Don't,' he said softly. 'You're not frightened of me.'

His silence commanded an answer. Rachel swallowed again.

'No,' she agreed at last. It was a whisper, no more.

He reached down and took her hand away. She could feel in the darkness that he never took his eyes from her.

He bent and set his lips very gently to the vulnerable place at the base of her throat where her pulse raced. A wild sensation swept through her.

It was like fire. Gasping, Rachel fell back. Her throat arched under his touch. Her hands reached for him. She was making small, desperate sounds that shocked some remote part of her brain. It was not the part that was in control.

Her unpractised hands tore at unfamiliar zips and fastenings, fumbling, impatient. He laughed a little and helped her. His breathing was nearly as ragged as her own.

And then he rid her of her nightdress with a speed that was not unpractised at all. It was a small thing—she barely noticed it in the headlong rush to strip away every last covering—but just for a moment she must have hesitated. He stopped as if she had stabbed him.

'No,' he said with deadly softness.

Rachel was bewildered. The sensation of skin against skin was so exquisite that she could hardly bear it. She did not know why he had stilled.

'What is it?' Her voice was slurred, almost unrecognisable.

'No more holding out.'

He was beside her, leaning over her, one hand in her hair. She moved her head restlessly and his hand tightened.

'No more.'

'I'm not holding out.' She sounded frantic, and very young all of a sudden. 'I'm not.'

She was almost faint with the intensity of her need. He must know that, with all that experience of his. Even in her extremity, the distant thought made her wince.

It seemed he did. He bent his head and kissed one lifting nipple slowly. Rachel cried out.

'Maybe not here.' She thought she could feel him smiling against the sensitised skin. His mouth drifted with agonising slowness to her other breast. She moaned. 'Or here.'

He reared up and looked down at her, taking her by surprise. Her eyes flew open. In the room's shadows his eyes were glittering. He touched her temple.

'But in there.' His voice was harsh. 'You're not giving an inch in there, are you?'

'What do you want me to give?' she whispered.

He almost shook her. 'Tell me. *Tell* me.'

So he wanted the complete surrender, in form, spelled out loud so that she could never pretend to forget again. Rachel thought she would die of shame. She shut her eyes tight. 'I want you.'

There, that would do, wouldn't it? That had to be what he wanted. It was the victory he had sought since the first moment he'd realised who she was on Monday.

It seemed it was not enough. He still held off from her.

'Tell me the truth. The whole truth. What happened all those years ago. *Why.*'

There was no escape. Despising herself, Rachel gave him the capitulation she knew he wanted.

'I always wanted you. In the Villa Azul. Afterwards. You said I did and you were right. I—never stopped wanting you.'

'Even when you ran out on me?'

She thought her heart would break. 'Even when I left,' she said steadily.

He bent his head. She thought he was going to kiss her mouth at last, but he was burying his face in her hair. His hands were unsteady.

'God, why did we waste so much time?' he said hoarsely.

He did kiss her then. For a moment she was startled. He kissed her almost with desperation. But then, twining herself round him, Rachel thought, How could I have held out for so long? She was wrought to fever pitch, responding to his every touch, every murmur, almost every pulse beat.

Just for a moment he paused, cupping her face between his hands. She was breathing hard but he stilled her.

'We're supposed to be responsible adults.' There was that unmistakable note of laughter in his voice. He groped for his jacket and retrieved a small packet. He dropped it into her hand. 'Though you almost make me forget.'

Rachel's heart contracted. Then memory or instinct took over entirely. She stopped thinking at all.

Later they lay quiet, her head on his chest. It rose and fell with his quiet breathing. She thought he was asleep. His hand was curved round her shoulder as if he was saying, She is mine.

She should have resented that, Rachel thought drowsily, but she did not. She was touched to the heart by that small gesture of possession. Moved by something she did not understand, she kissed his chest quickly, shyly. As she drifted into sleep she was happier than she had ever been in her life.

When she woke it was different—altogether different. Riccardo was dressed and looking out of the window. The world beyond the window was grey with morning rain. Inside the atmosphere was almost as chilly.

Rachel struggled to full wakefulness, rubbing her eyes. 'What is it?'

He did not look at her. 'What is Torrance to you?'

'Colin?' Rachel blinked.

'The man you were having dinner with last night.'

'Why?'

He said with apparent irrelevance, 'You wouldn't have dinner with me.'

Rachel stared at his stiff back. 'What?'

'Do you know what you looked like?'

She did not answer. He did not seem to expect her to. He swung round.

'Lovers. That's what you looked like. I thought— But I was obviously wrong. Is he your lover, Rachel?'

She was so taken aback that she could not think of a thing to say. Riccardo seemed to take her silence for agreement. He laughed harshly.

'Has anyone ever known what they were getting in you, I wonder?'

Rachel shook her head, bewildered. 'I don't know what you're talking about.'

'Colin Torrance pushed a message under your door last night. Presumably when you and I were making love.'

Rachel winced. Riccardo was crumpling a piece of paper in his hand. He lobbed it across the room savagely.

'Message?'

'He wants to make sure you'll be discreet,' Riccardo told her. His voice was soft but it sounded like poison.

Rachel gasped.

'Look, you've got this all wrong,' she said, reaching out a pleading hand. 'Last night it was work. He sounded off about our boss. He just wants to make sure that I won't spill the beans when I get back to London.' Her voice rose on a note of desperation. 'He's a colleague, that's all.'

'You mean, just like I am?' Riccardo said. His smile was like a slap in the face.

Rachel's hand fell. She was growing angry.

She said with precision, 'I don't know what you are. Or what you think you're doing here. Are you going to tell me?'

He showed his teeth. 'I told you. Finishing unfinished business. And I'm the man you ran out on.'

'The man I—?' She looked round the room, on an outward puff of disbelief. 'You mean all those years ago? After the Villa Azul? I ran out on *you*?'

He said harshly, 'You knew where to find me. If you wanted to. I didn't know where to start.'

'You could have found out. Anders knew. Well, he could have asked Judy. At least . . .' Rachel remembered her father's frozen silence, the complete breakdown of communication.

'Judy said you'd moved out. So did your father. I concluded you wouldn't talk to me.'

Rachel was confounded. She had blamed him, *hated* him for not finding her. It had never occurred to her that he could have looked without success.

'I came to London. Then my uncle had his heart attack. The company went into a tail-spin. I had to deal with it. I went back to New York but I hired a detective. Another blank. Your father sent him away too. There were no records of you anywhere—no credit cards, no employment references.' His voice grew bitter suddenly. 'Of course, I didn't realise how young you were. I never thought of telling him to tour the schools.'

Rachel said numbly, 'I'd left school. I was staying with friends all through the summer. I never went to university. I got a live-in job . . . oh, October some time.'

'The detective just sent me a nil report. He said there was no point in going on. By that time he must have thought I was chasing a woman who didn't want anything to do with me, hounding her against her will.'

'No.' It was a strangled protest. She leaned forward. There was a moment of absolute silence. Now—*now*— it seemed they were telling each other the truth at last.

'So did I,' he said levelly.

It hung in the air, waiting for an answer. Rachel moistened her lips. This had to be the most important answer of her life.

The telephone by her bed rang shrilly. She jumped. Riccardo raised his head. His eyes were hard. The moment of possible understanding had gone as if it had never been.

'If that's Torrance, get rid of him,' he said curtly.

But it was not Colin Torrance. It was Hugh. There had been an all-night party. The neighbours had complained to the police about the noise. And Alexandra had run off with Theo Judd.

CHAPTER TEN

RICCARDO took charge. While Rachel packed and cancelled her meeting he organised their journey. The first flight available was late afternoon.

'Then hire a plane,' he told his assistant curtly.

They flew back on a ten-seater executive jet. Rachel tried to thank him. He shrugged.

'I take it this is the boyfriend who makes you uneasy.'

'How did you know that?'

He gave a wintry smile. 'I listen when you talk to me. It doesn't happen so often.'

Which silenced Rachel.

The chauffeur, whom she recognised, met them at the airport. Riccardo handed her into the car and then went round and got in beside her. Rachel was startled.

'There's no need—' she began.

'Relax. You should know by now I'm not into kidnapping,' he said drily.

'But—'

'You're an independent woman and you can handle anything that hits you,' he supplied. 'I know. But this time you don't need to.'

Rachel stared. As if he could not help himself, he buffed her chin lightly. He was smiling, though it did not warm his eyes.

'Why don't you just lie back and enjoy?'

She had no answer.

When they got there, the house was a shambles. Not a room was unscathed. Rachel looked round the ruined hallway and sat down.

'Some party,' said Riccardo, his brows lifting.

Hugh came out of the kitchen. His face was worried. Rachel looked at him. 'What on earth happened?'

166

Hugh shuffled uncomfortably. 'The girls were all doing some project for school. It looked all right. I—er—went to a movie.'

'All night?' exclaimed Rachel.

Hugh looked even more uncomfortable. Riccardo touched her shoulder.

'I don't suppose he went alone. Then afterwards they went on somewhere to talk about the movie. Right?' he suggested in a tone of unholy amusement.

'Right.' Hugh nodded, relieved.

'And when he got back the party was in full swing.'

'Well—er—no. It was over. The—er—police ...'

Rachel moaned. 'We were raided by the police?'

'It wasn't that bad,' Hugh hastened to assure her. 'Not raided. Just some neighbours complaining about the noise. When the Old Bill turned up, Theo took off.'

'Taking Lexy with him?'

Hugh looked guilty. 'No. That was later. I was pretty wound up when I found out what had been going on. We had a row. She said she was going to Theo and steamed out.'

Rachel stared at him, appalled.

'That was when I called you,' he finished defensively.

'Oh, Lord.' She did not know what to do. She could not think straight. She put her hands to her face. It was cold. 'What exactly did she say?'

Riccardo put both hands on her shoulders. The warmth of his palms felt as if it could put life into her shivering frame. Hardly knowing what she did, she put her head on one side and rubbed her cheek against the back of his hand. Briefly, his fingers tightened so hard that she felt as if he had taken hold of her bones.

But all he said was, 'Do you know where she went?'

Hugh was startled. 'Theo—'

'Bravado,' pointed out Riccardo. 'Never under-estimate bravado. Have you actually checked?'

Hugh had not. Rachel got up.

'Gilly,' she said.

But Alexandra was not staying with her friend. Susanna was not at school after the night's excesses, however, and she knew Theo's address. She sounded worried at the thought that Alexandra might be with him there. Rachel wrote down the address, trying not to panic. When she rang off, Riccardo took the paper from her.

'I'll go.'

'But—'

'I bet she isn't there. She's probably sulking in a diner somewhere, writing her entrance speech. You stay here and wait for her. If by some chance she is there, she'll come back with me,' he said with superb arrogance.

Rachel found she did not doubt him.

He went. She shook herself and took charge of her life again. As a first step she sent Hugh to school with a note to excuse his lateness. Then she telephoned her secretary.

'No problem,' Mandy said. 'Colin's been in touch. He said it was a real help to talk things through with you. Even though you weren't there, he took a tough line this morning. The board have agreed. He says you don't need to go back unless you want to.'

'Great,' said Rachel, looking ruefully at the chaos that was her sitting room. 'I'll pass. Give him my congratulations. I won't be in until tomorrow. You can get me at home if you want me.'

She changed into her oldest clothes and set about restoring the house to normal. She was just finishing the stairs when she heard the sound of an engine. She straightened. The doorbell rang imperatively. She almost fell in her eagerness to reach it.

Riccardo was standing there, holding onto a wildly protesting Alexandra. True to his prediction, he had brought her home. Rachel was so thankful that she just flung her arms round her in a bear hug. Her stepdaughter clung.

Riccardo moved them in from the doorstep and closed the door behind them.

'She is unharmed,' he said to Rachel over the top of the weeping girl's head.

'Thank God.' She brushed the lacquered spikes of hair back. 'Oh, Lexy. What a fright you gave us.'

But Alexandra's tears were due to rage and affronted dignity, not guilt. She flung herself out of Rachel's arms and retreated to the wall. Her face was streaked with the remains of last night's make-up. She was in a tearing temper.

'Then it must be for the first time in your life,' she spat. 'You never notice what I'm doing except to spoil things.'

'That's not true—'

'Yes, it is. I talk and talk and talk and you just don't *listen* to me.'

Rachel was strongly moved to shout back in the same vein. She repressed it. Instead she sat down and folded her hands quietly in her lap.

'I'm listening now.'

Alexandra looked disgusted, and very young. 'Don't tell me—the thought police kick in.' She sounded young too. 'A final appeal to my conscience?'

Rachel shook her head. 'No appeal to anything.'

The front door banged and Hugh burst in. He was looking embarrassed and worried. But most of all he was just plain furious.

'You're back are you, you pinhead. Do you know the trouble you've caused?'

Rachel said warningly, 'Hugh—'

'Well, at least I—'

'Lexy—'

'You're no better than a groupie, running after Theo Judd with your tongue hanging out.'

Alexandra gave a scream of outrage and launched herself at Hugh. Riccardo caught her before she hit him.

'That's enough.' His tone was quiet but there was something in it that stopped both of them in their tracks.

He let Alexandra go and stepped back.

'Rachel has put her job on hold to listen to you today,' he told Alexandra crisply. 'So talk.'

She tossed her head, glaring at her brother. 'With the last ninety-year-old A-level entrant taking notes?'

Hugh started forward in protest. Riccardo stopped him. He put just a simple hand on his arm but it was enough. Riccardo was watching Rachel unblinkingly.

Alexandra sneered, 'Go on, say it, Hugh. I'm too young. Too stupid. I'm only a kid. I should listen to the grown-ups—and sensible, responsible people like boring Hugh Gray.'

There was a harsh pause. Rachel thought that, under the sneering expression, Alexandra did not look too far from tears. Her heart contracted with sympathy.

She stood up and went forward.

'Hugh doesn't have to say it, Lexy,' she said quietly. 'I will. I should have done a long time ago. I tried but—' She broke off, shaking her head.

There was no point in excusing herself. She had failed her stepdaughter. She must not fail her any more.

'I know you don't want to believe me, Lexy. But age does make a difference.'

'Yeah. I've noticed.'

'At your age people can think they want things—really want them—which they just don't understand a couple of years later, or sometimes a couple of months later.'

Alexandra snorted. 'I'll grow out of it?'

'If you want to put it like that.'

Even as she said it, Rachel knew it was a mistake. She did not want to let Alexandra down but this was not the way. She was going to have to be more honest than that.

Her stepdaughter smiled nastily. 'You mean I'll grow out of sex? Just like you did?'

Rachel's head went back as if at a blow. Across the room Riccardo went very still. Nobody noticed except Rachel. She was desperately conscious of that silent, watchful presence in the doorway. It made what she knew she had to do a thousand times more difficult.

Alexandra flung her chin up defiantly. 'Well, I don't want to grow out of it. I'd rather take a few risks on people. At least I'll still be *alive*.'

Rachel looked down at her hands. 'Well, at least you know Theo is a risk.'

She looked up quickly and caught Alexandra's involuntary recoil. Hugh drew in an audible breath.

Alexandra said furiously, 'You're trying to trick me into saying I don't trust him.'

'No.'

'Yes, you are. You said—'

'Theo is a risk. He is. We all are. Sex is. Life is.' She gave a little self-mocking laugh. 'My job at the bank is called risk management. It doesn't begin to look at the really big risks. And do you know what the biggest risk is, Lexy?'

'Families,' snarled Alexandra.

Rachel shook her head. 'Love.'

Alexandra cast her eyes to heaven. 'Oh, p-lease.'

Rachel winced. She drew in a careful breath. This was worse than she had imagined.

'I mean it,' she said steadily. 'Anything else, you've got a sporting chance. You can be careful, look at the downside, make a reasoned assessment, guard yourself if necessary. You know that. You know all about safe sex—you told me.' She carefully avoided looking at Riccardo. 'But there's no such thing as safe love. Once you're in love with someone, you're hooked. Vulnerable for ever. If they're hurt, you're hurt. If they cheat you, or let you down or just get bored...'

Rachel's voice cracked. She gave a quick shrug, turning her head away to hide her expression. She prayed that the immense effort that this was costing her did not show.

'There's nothing you can do to protect yourself against any of that. It hurts. It goes on hurting until, if you get really lucky, you fall out of love. Even then—well, you never forget what it was like. To be that badly hurt, I mean. It lasts. It's like a sort of poison you never get out of your system. You think you're cured and then—

crash!—something reminds you and it's back, just as bad as ever.'

In the doorway Riccardo was standing like stone. Rachel thought, He knows it all now. It lacerated her. But there was no hope that he would be misled. He was the cleverest man she had ever known and he knew her better than anyone else had ever done. However much she might be able to convince Hugh or Alexandra, or even Gilly, that this was pure neutral observation, she would never get away with it with Riccardo. He knew it was personal. And he knew it was the unadorned truth.

In which case he would also know—or be able to work out all too soon—that she had fallen in love with him at the Villa Azul. That she been in love with him ever since. And that she had been in love with him last night.

Oh, Lexy, she thought, if you knew what I am doing for you.

Alexandra's eyes were fever-bright. 'I can take care of myself.'

Rachel felt the thread by which she was holding onto her temper tighten. How much self-revelation was her stepdaughter going to demand?

She said levelly, 'In most circumstances, I agree with you.'

'Well, then—'

'In *most* circumstances. You're practical. You're intelligent. You're brave. You're just not—' she searched for the right words '—very strong yet.'

Alexandra looked down her nose. 'Tosh.'

Rachel's temper snapped. 'You've got a brain. Use it. You've as good as admitted you know Theo is a risk. He is worse than that. He is a dead-certain disaster and everyone in this room knows it. Including you.'

It was the worst thing she could possibly have said. Alexandra flung herself away, a muscle in her cheek jumping. She picked up her bag defiantly. Hugh shook himself free of Riccardo's restraining hand.

Rachel was the only one in the room who did not move. She said quietly, 'It's not tosh. It's the truth. You're going to give him your heart and all he wants is to score.'

It was a brutal thing to say. They all knew it. Alexandra stopped dead. Rachel could feel everyone in the room staring at her, shocked. But the only expression she saw was Riccardo's. He was looking appalled.

Alexandra turned. Her face was so white that you could see the streaks of make-up where she had applied the false tan unevenly. Her mouth looked pinched suddenly.

'Have you got any proof?' she whispered.

'Oh, Lexy,' Rachel was almost crying herself.

'*Have* you?'

Rachel averted her eyes from Riccardo's expression.

'His whole life, love. You know it in your heart of hearts. He won't tell you anything about himself. Will he?'

Riccardo was very still. Alexandra did not notice but Rachel was so conscious of him that her bones burned. If she ended up without a shred of dignity after today— well, that was what she had been prepared for when she'd started this. There was no point in stopping now.

She said, 'He has his own friends. You don't even know who they are. Or what they do. You're just a— game for him.'

Riccardo drew a sharp breath. Rachel ignored him. Alexandra looked like the child she had been not so long ago, crying out with nightmares, wanting a reassuring story before she went back to sleep.

Rachel's heart twisted. For a moment she almost softened. But this was too important. She could not afford to weaken now, even though she felt as if she was scraping every word up from her deepest hurt.

'When I was young I did something very similar,' she said painfully.

The figure at the door stiffened. Rachel saw it and looked quickly away. Across the room his eyes were as black as coals in a great fire.

She said to Alexandra, 'I was older than you are. There was less excuse. Like you, I thought I knew what I was doing. I thought I was willing to take the consequences, live completely for a burning moment, then pay the price.' She laughed harshly. 'Joan of Arc has a lot to answer for.'

Riccardo did not move. But she could feel him watching her as if he had an arc light trained on her.

'It's not like that. When you're young, sex and love and the imagination are all tied up together. A sort of emotional primeval soup. It's no one's fault. It's just a stage of development. We all go through it. But if you're not careful, if you commit yourself too soon, too deep, you burn up all the oxygen too soon.'

Alexandra was staring. So was everyone else. Rachel felt naked. Riccardo would not be the only one who knew, after this.

She said, with the courage of exhaustion, 'You said you don't think I'm quite alive—not in the way that you are, willing to take a chance on Theo. I can't deny it. So ask yourself why I'm like that. And see if you can avoid going the same way.'

There was a truly horrible silence. Everybody was trying to avoid her eyes. Except for Riccardo. He seemed as if he could not look away. He looked stunned.

Rachel felt as if she had no shred of dignity left, no single defence that Riccardo could not see through as easily as gauze. But she lifted her chin and outfaced him.

As their eyes met, it was like an electric shock. Rachel could feel it—could feel Riccardo feel it too. It seemed to drive him backwards with its force.

Alexandra gave a shattering sob.

'Oh *Rachel*.'

She flung herself against her stepmother's breast. Rachel's arms closed round the slight figure automatically. Across the dark head her eyes stayed on Riccardo, faintly questioning.

He looked back for what seemed like an eternity. She could not begin to read his expression. Then he made a quick, wholly characteristic gesture, setting himself at a distance from the tableau.

And, as Rachel stroked Alexandra's hair with a hand that shook, Riccardo turned on his heel and walked out of her house.

CHAPTER ELEVEN

IT WAS a bad moment. Rachel watched him go and felt as if the rest of her life had just left. What has happened to me? she thought. She held Alexandra and made soothing noises mechanically while she slowly allowed herself to realise the truth.

Nine years had passed and nothing had changed. She was still in love with Riccardo di Stefano. And she still did not have the faintest idea how he felt.

Except that he's just walked out, she reminded herself. That might just give you a clue.

She kept half an ear open for the telephone for the rest of the day. It rang but it was never Riccardo. And tomorrow he would be flying back to New York. Rachel stayed up till midnight but Riccardo did not come back to the house either. It was a tough day.

Breakfast the next morning felt more like a duel than a meal. Alexandra might have been feeling chastened but that did not change her attitude to her brother. Rachel made toast and refereed until they were both persuaded to go to school. She sank back, exhausted, but there was no respite. She had to go to work and she was already late.

'I know. I know,' she said to Geoff as she slid in through the swing-doors. 'Again. Mr Jensen been asking for me?'

The security guard shifted uncomfortably. 'Not Mr Jensen.'

Rachel raised her eyes to heaven. 'Clients! My stars. How do they find these things out? I was supposed to be in Aberdeen. Some of them must know when I change my toothpaste.'

Geoff grinned and indicated the private lift with a raised eyebrow.

'You're probably right,' agreed Rachel. 'The back stairs it is.'

She slipped round his desk gratefully. She was not so grateful when she reached her own floor. Her imagined client was already there, propping up the wall. He was clearly waiting for her.

Rachel's heart lurched. She felt a rush of warmth so great that it must have shown on her face. And then she remembered that he had walked out. She had no right to feel that gladness at the sight of him. She was only laying up hurt for herself all over again.

She nearly retreated back into the lift. But the doors had closed. So there was no alternative. Rachel stepped forward, her head high.

'Good morning.'

But Riccardo seemed to have lost patience with the courtesies. His jaw was tight. He had every appearance of a man looking for a fight.

'No, it isn't. It's a bloody awful morning. Where the hell have you been?'

Rachel stared. 'Keeping my stepchildren from each other's throats and getting them off to school,' she said literally.

His eyes narrowed. 'I thought nothing came between you and your work?'

She remembered telling him that. She shrugged uneasily. 'Well—'

'Or are children different? Is it only lovers who don't count?'

This was a battle with a vengeance. Rachel's face flamed. 'We are not lovers,' she choked. 'You have no right—'

'I have the right,' Riccardo said softly. His eyes were narrowed to slits of fury. 'I stood there yesterday and had to listen to you telling Lexy things you should have told me nine years ago. Don't talk to me about rights.'

'Oh,' said Rachel.

'And as for us not being lovers—what do you think we have been doing all this week?'

Rachel looked anxiously along the corridor. Fortunately there was no one in sight. Not that it would have deterred Riccardo from his purpose. That was all too evident. Rachel pressed her hands to her cheeks. Her face felt incandescent.

'That was just sex,' she managed.

Riccardo's lips tightened. 'Once. We slept together once.'

She flung her head back and glared at him. 'Quite.'

There was a sizzling silence.

'My God,' he said slowly. 'And I thought I never took anything on trust. I'm an amateur compared to you.'

Rachel sent him a glittering smile. 'Experience.'

She began to turn away. He stopped her by the simple expedient of putting a hand on her arm. Rachel's heart lurched again. The electrical recognition was still there.

In love with him and her body recognising his lightest touch! Heaven help me, she thought.

She shook him off and started off down the corridor. Her breathing was rapid. She hoped that he would ascribe it to the speed of her steps.

Riccardo kept pace with her. 'You can't walk away from me this time,' he told her quietly. 'I'm not letting it happen again.'

Rachel did not look at him. 'You have no choice.'

He gave a soundless laugh. 'Oh, yes, I have. This time I know what I'm dealing with.'

She stopped and swung round, glaring. 'If you're referring to the fact that I work for Bentley's, forget it. I can get another job, like *that*.' She snapped her fingers.

He looked amused for a moment. 'I'm sure you can. I wouldn't dream of using professional blackmail.'

'Then—'

'On the other hand,' he went on smoothly, 'we will be seeing each other all the time. Wouldn't it be better to clear the air?'

Rachel looked at him scornfully. 'Quite unnecessary. The first time we met you didn't know who I was. We can go back to that.'

Riccardo shook his head. 'Unrealistic. And I knew precisely who you were the moment you turned round when we were alone in the boardroom.' He laughed softly. 'Wild red hair all over the place, glaring at me. Of course I knew. I just had not made up my mind what to do about it.'

'And when did you decide?' Rachel said, goaded.

'At the board meeting, of course. Watching you fight for what you believed in. I thought, She hasn't changed.' He smiled down at her. 'I thought—I want her.'

Rachel was shaken. She had a sudden memory, almost physical, of the feeling she had had that first day when she'd seen him in the corridor. The precipice was still there; the mountain was still at her back. If anything it was even more cold and frightening.

Only, this time she knew what it was she was afraid of. It was not Riccardo di Stefano. It was herself. After all this time she was still in love with him. It looked as if she always would be. And all he could say was that he wanted her.

Rachel moistened dry lips. She said, 'Well, it may be a shock to you but you're not the only one involved here. I've taken some decisions too.' She turned and faced him. 'I don't want to see you again, Riccardo. Please respect that. If you don't, I shall leave Bentley's.'

She turned away before she could see his reaction. She could feel him watching her as she walked down the corridor to her own office. But he did not follow her.

In her room she sank bonelessly into her chair. She felt slightly sick. She dropped her head in her hands. What had she done?

I couldn't have taken it again, she told herself. I had to send him away. So Alexandra was right, said another part of her mind. You may not have outgrown normal feelings but you've dealt yourself out of living. Is that what you really want?

She rubbed her eyes. 'What I really want is Riccardo di Stefano. For ever.' She said it out loud. It sounded even worse than it felt. She winced. 'Face it. For ever is not his style. So I can't have him. So get on with your life, Rachel.'

She tried. She really tried for the whole day. By the end of it, her temples were throbbing with the effects of her mighty efforts. It did not seem to make much difference. Every time the door opened she looked up, half in hope, half in dread. It was never Riccardo.

When it was completely dark outside, she stood up, her hands to her aching back. She looked at her watch. Seven o'clock. He must be halfway over the Atlantic by now.

Her computer beeped. Wearily Rachel pushed buttons to retrieve the message. It was from Mandy.

Rachel, Hugh rang. Gas switched off at home. There's no heating and no hot water. So he and Alexandra have gone to Gilly's. I booked you a room at the Langbourne. Have a good weekend.

Great, thought Rachel. Still, thank God for secretaries with the initiative to save her from a freezing house. She rang Gilly.

'Yes, the children are here. Don't worry about a thing. They're actually talking to each other.'

'They must be up to something,' said their fond stepmother. She sent them her love and went off to the discreetly smart hotel that Mandy had organised.

When she arrived the luxury of the suite made her raise her eyebrows. It was a new hotel with a reputation to make but, even so, this was not going to be within her normal price range. There had to be a mistake over the booking. She was picking up the telephone to query it when there was a knock at the door.

Rachel got up and opened it. It was the man who should have just about been watching the end of the last in-flight movie coming into JFK. She fell back.

'Thank you,' he said, taking it as an invitation. He strolled in and closed the door behind him. 'Frankly, I've had enough of slithering round hotel rooms in the dark. It may be your fantasy but it is not comfortable.'

Rachel backed before him. 'My fantasy?' she said, totally bewildered. 'What do you mean?'

He laughed. 'What did you think I was doing, creeping into your room in Aberdeen? Not my usual form. But you said you could imagine your hero breaking into your room at midnight.'

'I didn't,' she gasped.

'Oh, but you did. "Like something out of a silent movie,"' he reminded her helpfully. 'I recall it clearly.'

Rachel had a blinding flash of memory. She had said something very like that, she realised. Now she thought about it, she could even remember when. When his chauffeur had carried her off to lunch, if she was right.

'You didn't take that seriously?'

'I take everything you say to me seriously.' Riccardo paused, then added thoughtfully, 'I drew the line at the mask, though.'

Rachel sat down on the edge of the bed rather suddenly. 'You're crazy.'

That interested him. 'Do you think so? I thought a mask might be difficult to explain if you lost your head and screamed for the management.'

'If *I* lost my head— Oh! You're impossible.'

A half-smile curled the handsome mouth. 'Incidentally,' he said idly, 'why didn't you, do you think?'

Rachel glowered. 'Yell for the hotel manager? I should have done, the moment you showed up,' she hissed. 'I can't think why I didn't.'

His smile grew. 'You could have been half-asleep,' Riccardo said helpfully.

Rachel was outraged. 'You thought I was half-asleep and you still invaded my privacy?'

He chuckled. He did not need to remind her exactly how thoroughly he had invaded. Rachel began to feel very unsure all of a sudden.

He took pity on her and sat down—on the sofa, not next to her on the bed. 'To be honest, it was not the way I planned it at all,' he admitted. 'I arrived later than I expected. You were already having dinner. With Torrance.'

He sounded grim about that. Rachel remembered his anger over Colin. Had he been jealous? But, if so, why? You were not jealous about people unless you loved them. Were you? She almost demanded an explanation. But her courage failed. It would be so humiliating if she was wrong. She began to tremble, though.

Riccardo went on levelly, 'I decided I'd wait. Then I got a call from London. By the time I'd done with that you seemed to be asleep. I went back to my room.' He paused. 'I would have left you alone but you called out. It might have been a dream but I could not be sure. So I came in to you. And what happened, happened.'

Rachel remembered those dreams. She found she believed him. But she was not going to let him get away with it so easily.

'That still doesn't explain what you were doing in the room next to mine,' she pointed out. 'With the connecting door unlocked.'

Riccardo looked at her for a long moment. He showed no sign of remorse.

'Careful planning. Plus a good eye for an opportunity when it presented itself.' He sounded smug.

Rachel bounced on the spot, revolted. 'I have not,' she told him, 'presented myself to you in any way.'

He laughed again. 'Don't I know it,' he said ruefully. 'I've never cancelled so many meetings in my life. The day before yesterday. Yesterday. Next week's on hold. All thoroughly out of character. And all your fault.'

It shook her. She said, 'I don't believe it.'

He shrugged. 'Believe it or not. It's the truth.'

He leaned forward and smiled straight into her eyes. Rachel felt her senses reel. She could feel herself being drawn off down a path she had never dreamed of, with only Riccardo to show the way.

She brought herself back to the matter in hand with a mental shake. The other road was much too dangerous.

'How the hell did you get yourself installed in the room next to mine anyway?'

'Enterprise and a romantic receptionist.'

'*What?*'

He stood up and came over to the bed at last. She had discarded her jacket when she'd come in and now he undid the top two buttons of her businesslike blouse. He pushed it off one shoulder. Rachel's mouth went dry but she did not stop him.

Riccardo bent his head and began to kiss her shoulder without urgency. She felt the response in spite of herself.

She said in a high, hurried voice, 'Who told you the receptionist was romantic?'

'She did.'

His mouth barely touching her skin, he travelled along her collar-bone. Rachel could feel herself begin to shake. She could also feel herself tipping backwards dangerously. She swallowed and tried to concentrate on other things.

'When?' It was not much more than a squeak, she thought, disgusted with herself.

He lifted his head to answer her. Her eyes were losing focus. She knew he was smiling from his voice.

'When I arrived. I was annoyed about being late. She thought I was your husband. She said you weren't expecting me.' His eyes gleamed. 'What else could I do but agree?'

Rachel swallowed. 'Clever.'

'Lucky,' he said modestly.

He kissed her throat lingeringly. She felt herself sway back another dangerous ten degrees. 'And all because you *want* me,' she said bitterly. 'It hardly seems worth it, does it?'

There was a short, startled pause. Then Riccardo sat
up. It was so far from what Rachel had been expecting
that she collapsed in sheer astonishment. He looked
down at her but he made no move to touch her.

'I think we may be at cross purposes here,' he said in
quite a different tone. 'What exactly do you think is
going on between you and me?'

Rachel winced. But she said steadily enough, 'You
want to sleep with me. You're an attractive man and you
don't see why you shouldn't have what you want.'

He looked as if he could not believe his ears.

Hurting herself more than him, she went on in a hard
voice, 'I don't know if that's just because you think it
was an untidy ending all those years ago, or whether you
want to be the one to walk away this time—'

'Stop it.'

She fell silent. His eyes were blazing. She would not
have thought that the cool Riccardo di Stefano could
look so wild.

'You insult both of us.'

'Can the truth be an insult?'

'Truth!' He stood up on a surge of contempt. 'Let me
show you the truth, Rachel McLaine. Then you tell me
if I want to be the one who walks away.'

He strode across to a table under the window and
picked up a small box. It looked like a jeweller's box,
too big for a ring, too small for a necklace. He almost
threw it at Rachel.

'Look.'

She struggled up and opened it. Inside there was
something that looked like a pattern of tissue-paper,
brown and ginger with a hint of apricot. She looked up,
puzzled.

'What is it?'

He took it out of her hands. He handled it very gently.
Rachel thought, He's done this a thousand times before.

He turned the thing round, disposing it tenderly over
her palm, as if were a small animal. Rachel looked down

at it. It began to fold into a familiar shape: a dried trumpet flower.

She said slowly, 'Hibiscus.'

'You were wearing it. Do you remember? When I went to your cabin, that was all that was left. It was tucked down between the pillows.'

Rachel touched one long dried petal with a fingertip. 'It must have fallen out of my hair. You kept it?'

He looked down at her, his mouth wry. 'If it hadn't been for that, I might have started to think you had never existed at all.'

She felt humbled.

Riccardo sat down beside her. He took her hand.

'Why did you disappear like that?' he asked quietly.

She folded her lips together. It hurt to remember. But with that dead flower in her hand she could not tell him anything but the truth.

'My father,' she said honestly. 'You don't know what it was like. He...' Her voice became suspended. She touched the flower, as if it were a talisman, and went on bravely. 'His business was in trouble. He'd married a woman half his age. She wanted to leave him. The easiest thing was to blame me.'

Riccardo stared. 'Blame you? Why? How?'

'I never thought a daughter of mine would behave like a slut,' her father had said, white-lipped. 'Judy can't handle it. You embarrassed her too much. You're old enough to make your own way in the world and that's clearly what you want. Get out of this house now and don't come back.'

For years Rachel had suppressed it. Now she said, 'He was floundering. He felt a failure. If he kicked me out, he felt he had taken control of his life again for a bit. I suppose he thought he would have a better chance of mending things if he and Judy were alone together.'

Riccardo took her chin and turned it to him. 'Kicked you out?' he echoed. 'Are you serious?'

She shrugged.

'Oh, my love.' He sounded remorseful enough now.
'I didn't know. How could he? You were so young.' He
paused. 'I didn't know how young until this week. That
didn't make me feel any better either.'

Rachel touched his face.

'Not that young. I knew what I was doing.'

'Did you?' He searched her face. All of a sudden he
was desperately serious. 'Are you sure?'

'As sure as I am that I know what I'm doing now,'
she said.

Rachel put the flower back in its box very carefully.
She stood up and restored the box to the table. When
she came back to him, she was undoing the remaining
buttons of her blouse. She pulled it out of the waistband
of her skirt. Riccardo watched her gravely.

She slipped the blouse off her shoulders. It fell to the
floor unnoticed. His hands came out to her waist. He
tipped his head forward, resting it against her breasts
for a moment.

'I love you,' he said against her skin.

Rachel gave a long, sweet shiver. 'Make love to me,'
she whispered.

He looked up then. Whatever it was that he read in
her face, it seemed to lift a great burden off him. He
reached up and pulled her down to him. Rachel went
joyfully into his arms.

They lay breast to breast. Riccardo ran his hands over
her skin as if he were reminding himself of every curve
and texture.

'I never forgot.'

Rachel believed him. She was finding that her own
hands knew his body as well as if it were her own.

'Nor me.'

'You were so special. So *real*. You didn't fit in at the
Villa Azul. I did. I'd known people like that all my life.
Been part of them. Suddenly I didn't want that any
more.'

'No one would have guessed,' said Rachel ruefully.

He raised himself up on one elbow and looked down at her.

'I'd been working in Central America. I was running food into hill villages under siege. At the end of a year I was—different. I knew I had to go back to the family business. Apart from anything else, there were too many people dependent on it and no one but me to inherit. But I was kicking against it. When I talked to you, I thought, With her I could have some private happiness as well.'

Rachel smiled up at him. 'Only some?' she murmured.

He slid his hands under her, lifting her comprehensively against him. Her breath caught in her throat at the electric touch. Riccardo smiled, his eyes burning into hers.

'Maybe more than that.'

Rachel stretched against him provocatively.

Riccardo chuckled. 'Only a few hours ago you told me you never wanted to see me again,' he reminded her.

Rachel ran her hands through his hair, wonderingly. She could feel a laugh rising. 'Never underestimate the effects of bravado,' she reminded him solemnly.

She ran a finger up his spine. He gave a little shudder of sensation. She savoured it. He began to kiss her body slowly. It seemed as if he was taking infinite care of her. Rachel basked.

'I thought I meant it,' she murmured. 'At the time. Now you're here, I can't even remember why.' A thought occurred to her. 'How did you get here, by the way? Did you bribe my family or my secretary?'

She could feel him laugh against her skin. 'Does it matter?'

Her hands went round his body convulsively.

'No,' said Rachel on a long sigh. They both knew it was total surrender. 'No, it doesn't matter at all.'

He had reached the silken skin of her stomach. He raised his head and thoughtfully traced the contour of a hip-bone. He looked up, his eyes dancing.

'Then I'll tell you. It was both.'

'*What?*'

'But only on the strict understanding that I made an honest woman of you.'

She was blank. 'You're joking.'

Rachel tried to struggle up. Riccardo held her pinned in place with easy strength. He was laughing.

'On my honour. Marriage or nothing. Lexy was very precise. I think,' he added thoughtfully, 'she feels she's turning the tables a bit.'

'Lexy...?' Rachel was utterly bewildered. 'What are you talking about?'

'Conspiracy. Your nearest and dearest. Hugh turned off the gas. Lexy got the two of them beds for the night. Mandy booked the room I specified.' He leant back on one elbow. 'I organised it but cutting off the gas was Hugh's idea. I think that boy has promising managerial quality.'

Rachel was trying hard not to laugh. 'Really?'

'Really. Also bargaining skills. Same price as Lexy. Legal matrimony. Just what I had in mind, in fact.'

'What about me? What if I had something else in mind?' Rachel demanded, justifiably incensed.

He raised his eyebrows. 'Do you?'

Oh, that smile. It warmed you right through to your bones. It stopped the laughter right there in your throat. Which was not what Rachel wanted at all. She tossed her head, her loosened hair finally tumbling out of its pins, and would not answer.

Riccardo's hands moved, skilfully. Rachel gasped in spite of herself.

'Are you starting another fight, Rachel?' he murmured mischievously.

She moved, arching under his hands, reaching for him.

Her voice was thick with longing but there was answering laughter when she said, 'Only if you finish it.'

He bent his head to her mouth, the laughter dying on their lips.

'We'll finish it together,' he vowed.

☀SUMMER SEARCH

How would you like to win a year's supply of Mills & Boon®
books? Well you can and they're FREE! Simply complete the
competition below and send it to us by 31st December 1997.
The first five correct entries picked after the closing date will
each win a year's subscription to the Mills & Boon series of
their choice. What could be easier?

SPADE

SUNSHINE

PICNIC

BEACHBALL

SWIMMING

SUNBATHING

CLOUDLESS

FUN

TOWEL

SAND

HOLIDAY

W	Q	T	U	H	S	P	A	D	E	M	B
E	Q	R	U	O	T	T	K	I	U	I	E
N	B	G	H	L	H	G	O	D	W	K	A
I	I	O	A	I	N	E	S	W	Q	L	C
H	N	U	N	D	D	F	W	P	E	O	H
S	U	N	B	A	T	H	I	N	G	L	B
N	S	E	A	Y	F	C	M	D	A	R	A
U	B	P	K	A	N	D	M	N	U	T	L
S	E	N	L	I	Y	B	I	A	N	U	L
H	B	U	C	K	E	T	N	S	N	U	E
T	A	E	W	T	O	H	G	H	O	T	F
C	L	O	U	D	L	E	S	S	P	W	N

Please turn over for details of how to enter ☞

C7F

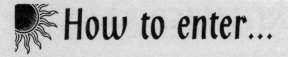# How to enter...

Hidden in the grid are eleven different summer related words. You'll find the list beside the word puzzle overleaf and they can be read backwards, forwards, up, down and diagonally. As you find each word, circle it or put a line through it. When you have found all eleven, don't forget to fill in your name and address in the space provided below and pop this page in an envelope (you don't even need a stamp) and post it today. Hurry competition ends 31st December 1997.

Mills & Boon Summer Search Competition
FREEPOST, Croydon, Surrey, CR9 3WZ
EIRE readers send competition to PO Box 4546, Dublin 24.

Please tick the series you would like to receive if you are a winner
Presents™ ❑ Enchanted™ ❑ Temptation® ❑
Medical Romance™ ❑ Historical Romance™ ❑

Are you a Reader Service™ Subscriber?   Yes ❑   No ❑

Ms/Mrs/Miss/Mr _____
(BLOCK CAPS PLEASE)

Address _____

_____

_____ Postcode _____

(I am over 18 years of age)